LEVELS OF DARKNESS

To Kevin
with love
From Sam

LEVELS OF DARKNESS

Published by Adam Rei Books
www.adamreibooks.com

ISBN: 978-1-911047-06-3

Cover Photography by Andrew Ellis

Designed by Print Tailors
www.printtailors.com

LEVELS OF DARKNESS

SAM RAILEY

ADAM REI BOOKS

For Nick and Siân

1

Maple Court, August 3, 1966, 9:00 a.m.

I spin round in the black leather swivel rocker. I remember Denise saying that the chair was too flash. But she still wanted to make love on it. We did and almost fell off.

I look blankly at what is going into the cardboard box. It's all in front of me on the teak coffee table, objects I'm leaving behind but will be unable to forget. *Scarne on Cards* is one of two books I'm keeping. I'm not sure why. I bought it four years ago when I first started to gamble. It's well-thumbed. At the time there wasn't much else out there. It gave me an edge and I started to play the odds.

◆

I loved gambling and dealing cards. On my nights off from dealing, I'd play poker or *chemin de fer*. I consistently won more than I lost. Gambling was my hobby, dealing chemmy was my job. I was a conductor controlling an orchestra, only instead of a baton I had a croupier's palette. I was in charge - the main act. The play and players need managing. Winners can be cruel, losers aggressive. The bigger the stakes the more chances of conflict. I had to be on top of running the game, making sure the rules were followed, no misdeals, bets placed properly and that the players behaved themselves.

I was good at it, rarely made a mistake, had no favourites, didn't put up with any nonsense. I maintained an entertaining, amicable atmosphere, not always easy with a group of volatile kibitzers – both on and off the table – giving unsolicited, often hilarious advice. I liked them all, enjoyed their company. The players liked me, treated me with respect, invited me to their homes. It was not a large city and the community of big gamblers was small. They were respectable businessmen, owners of local shops, cafes and restaurants, doctors, solicitors, chemists, mostly middle-aged men. There were young men in their late twenties and thirties and a few women, usually gamblers' wives.

I'd been in the business about eighteen months when I went to see the James Bond film, *Dr. No*. It had just come out. Even though I had read the book and all the other Bond novels, I was overwhelmed. That was me up there, dressed in a tuxedo, playing *chemin de fer*, gambling for high stakes. That's how I lived. Glamorous nights in London. Suites at the best hotels, the Dorchester, the May Fair, the newly opened Park Lane Hilton. Partying at The Scotch, at Annabel's. Jaunts to Monte Carlo, Las Vegas. I was on first name terms with stars and celebrities who only a few years earlier I would have queued to buy tickets to see.

I may not have been a secret agent but I did drive a fast luxury car, always carried a wad of cash. I played around in the bedroom and on the gaming tables more than anybody else I knew.

◆

I put *Scarne* in the cardboard box, an ordinary cardboard box, fifteen inches square. Once I've sealed it with sticky tape, I'll tie it with string and make a string handle the way Dad taught me. This box and a black leather suitcase with shiny red shot silk lining, filled with clothes, are all I have. Everything else has gone: the flat, the car, the jewellery, the suits, everything. I'm wearing jeans, a white T-shirt and brown suede desert boots, the kind of clothes I've never worn before.

I'm almost ready to walk out the door and that's it. All over.

The taxi is due at noon.

2

Maple Court, 9:05 a.m.

The black-lacquered wooden photograph frame protects the faded portraits of relatives I've only ever heard about. There's Uncle Adolphus with a walrus moustache and winged collar; Cousin Freddie and his girlfriend, smiling, holding hands; beautiful Cousin Fanny wearing a black, off the shoulder dress; and Uncle Arnold, gentle-looking, sporting a polka dot bow tie.

◆

Dad's unmarried sisters, Cissie and Sophie, lived next door. As soon as I went into their house I was compelled to look at the ornate frame with its four postcard-size photographs side by side. The Aunts spoke Yiddish, especially when they didn't want me to know what was going on but *ikh hob farshtanen a bisel*, I understood a little.

Every time they saw me looking at the photographs, there would be lots of whispering. Sophie would point and say, 'That's Arnold the doctor. We used to write to each other, but after 1939 we never heard from any of them again. Nobody found out what happened to them. We came from Przemyśl ... we'd been there for 900 years. They couldn't wait to get rid of us.'

The Aunts gave me the frame with its precious photographs so I should know who I was and where I came from.

I knew who I was. They called us Yids, sheenies. We were smart, well-dressed and when necessary, prepared to fight. *They*, were the English, *goyim*, who ate crap, got pissed and were always looking for a fight. For all that, when we prayed we asked the Almighty to protect the King and Queen and all the Royal Family.

We weren't religious, we just went to *shul* on *Yom Kippur* and a few other special Jewish holidays, always had chicken soup on a Friday night and lit candles. My sisters, Rita and Sandra, cleaned the house and brown-stoned the front steps in time for *Shabbos*. I was twelve years younger than Rita and four years younger than Sandra. We were a small family. My mum had six siblings but we rarely saw them. Sophie and Cissie were the only relatives we had close contact with. The others were usually referred to as 'those lot', meaning they were better off than us. They could hardly have been worse off.

◆

After wrapping the photograph frame in newspaper, I carefully place it in the cardboard box. I pick up the rosewood jewellery box. I had bought it for my watches, rings and cufflinks. It doesn't feel as heavy as it did before. All it holds now is a gold cigar cutter and two metal button badges, one with a washed-out coloured photograph of my grandmother printed on it and the other a black and white enamel CND badge – a present from Denise.

I changed from a punch to a cigar cutter after Wolfie gave me a lecture on the draw advantages of a cutter. 'Now, David,' he'd say, 'let me explain why the cutter is a much better tool than the punch, especially if you prefer a stronger, denser smoke. A punch can make the draw too tight – difficult to suck air through, whereas a high quality cutter...' And he'd be off.

◆

I met Wolfie just after Dad died. That's when everything changed.

Dad had the flu and it got worse. He had to go into

hospital and when I went to see him that evening he said, 'I've had enough of this, *Dovid*.' He used to call me that sometimes. He wasn't talking about the flu. He meant forty-five years of working in a sweatshop with a foreman standing over him holding a stopwatch, checking how fast he could cut patterns.

The next morning a policeman came to the house and told me Dad had died. I went round to my aunts' house. Cissie opened the front door and when I told her she looked at me and silently closed the door.

I thought I saw Dad more than once after he died. I'd follow a stranger for a few minutes before having to stop myself.

I was working on the markets when I met Wolfie. One of my pals was a *clapper* – somebody who knocks on doors, buying valuables from the unsuspecting. We used to meet in a so-called 'club for jewellers' in Fennel Street, a scruffy basement where clappers would go for a cup of tea, to play cards and to trade. I was waiting for my pal when this guy I didn't know came up to me and said, 'My name is Wolfie. I'd like to have a word with you.'

Wolfie was a croupier in a gambling club in the centre of Manchester. He said he was looking for a croupier to run a game of chemmy in his friend's new night club, the Whisky A Go Go. If I was interested he would show me the rudiments of the game and put me forward for the job.

I'd come across *chemin de fer* in Ian Fleming's first Bond

novel, *Casino Royale*, but I didn't really know what it was or what being a croupier entailed.

'Why me?' I asked.

He said, 'You're a good-looking lad and you remind me of someone I once knew. You could make a lot of money doing this, David,' he told me seriously.

I was intrigued enough to go to his place that afternoon. From the outside it looked like an ordinary house. That changed as soon as you walked through the front door. All the walls, ceilings and doors were painted bright orange. There was hardly any furniture except for a large dining table and four chairs. The walls were covered in dark, foreboding abstract paintings. By Wolfie. Countless similar canvases were stacked wherever there was available space. When he saw me looking – somewhat amazed – he laughed, 'Lesson number one, David. Nothing is ever what it seems.'

He was an enigmatic figure. He was in his early thirties, tall, good-looking, and with glasses tinted just enough so you couldn't tell if he was watching you or not. He looked more like a school teacher than a croupier in a gambling den. We sat down at the table and he produced a number of packs of cards, slowly explaining, '*Chemin de fer* attracts big gamblers, very big gamblers. It's the main card game in the European casinos of Deauville, Biarritz and on the Riviera. You probably don't know this, David –' (I didn't) '– but there's been a change in the law here and all sorts of gambling is now legal.

Chemmy is taking off in a big way and there are hardly any croupiers around.' As he was talking he was opening the packs and expertly shuffling the cards. 'Chemmy is a kind of banker game, played with six packs of cards. During the game they're kept in a wooden box, wedge-shaped, called a shoe. The shoe is passed anticlockwise around the table.'

Looking over the top of his glasses he seemed to be checking that he had my attention. I nodded to show him I was listening carefully.

'*Chemin de fer* is French for railway. Or iron path. People think the game is named after the movement of the shoe around the table, like a train.' He laughed.

'But ...?' I could see he wanted me to ask.

'The game is a version of *baccarat*, a French and Italian game, fifteenth century, long before the railway was invented. In those days the cards were placed in an iron box. That's how chemmy got its name.' He smiled. Having floored me with his erudition, he added, 'Not that it matters.' That was Wolfie.

Stacking the cards behind each other, their backs facing out, he began to deal. His speech was quiet, precise, and his accent faintly foreign. I couldn't place it. 'Remember, the croupier controls the game. Usually, no more than nine players take part. They play against each other and take turns at being the banker, putting in as much money as they want for the other players, the punters, to bet against. Starting with one card for the punters, then one for the banker, you deal two cards face down for the punters and two for the banker. Aces count as one, tens and court cards don't count and the tens unit is discounted. If either the punters or the bank have eight or nine they automatically win. If not, set rules determine whether or not the punters or the bank get a third card. Eventually, they show their cards and the nearest to nine wins. And that's it.' He must have noticed the blank look on my face. 'Don't worry I'll write the rules down for you. Study them. You'll soon get it.'

He continued dealing, turning the cards over, confirming the totals, declaring the winning hands, while I was concentrating, trying to take it all in.

'Look – an eight and a six, that's four not fourteen.' He was pointing at the cards.

'See, the bank's got a king and a seven - that's seven, the punters a four and a two – that's six, so the bank wins. Yes?'

I nodded but not with any certainty, it must be said.

'And then, when the bank loses, the shoe passes to the next player who has the option of being the banker or passing the shoe on.'

He never stopped demonstrating how to deal, describing the different hands, going over the rules. 'Now do you understand, David?' He would repeatedly ask this as he continued with his lecture demonstration. 'Now do you understand, David?' He made me deal endlessly, reminding me of the different rules, correcting my mistakes.

After three hours he said, 'Enough. I think you will be okay.' He sat back and looked at me. 'Well, David, yes or no?'

My head was spinning, but he had me hooked. Why not? I thought. I agreed to do it.

He took off his glasses, smiled and said, 'Good. I'm going to ring my friend Darius. I'll tell him you will be there tonight.'

That's why not, I thought. Fuck me, I didn't mean tonight.

But that night I did go to the Whisky A Go Go. Luckily for me some of the chemmy players were market workers I knew. With patience and lots of leg-pulling, they helped me deal. Whenever I wasn't sure what to do, one of the players would direct me. At one point I could see Darius, the owner, standing with his arms folded, watching what was going on – the players enjoying themselves. I got the nod of approval.

Overnight my wages increased tenfold.

I became a full time croupier, working a small room that overlooked the main club area, just big enough for one *chemin de fer* table. Eventually, there were three of us running the game, Eyeshadow Joe – who obviously wore a lot of eye shadow, Ray the trumpet player, and me.

Later I found out that Wolfie was Wolfgang Goldschmidt, the only survivor of a family of more than thirty. His mother and father, sister, two brothers and all his aunts, uncles and cousins, were murdered by the Nazis.

We would meet and drink schnapps. He always had a bottle to hand and every time would say the same thing after the first glass, 'Good, but not like my father made.' It was a ritual we both enjoyed. He would talk and I would listen.

... The boy would go with his mum to buy the Shabbos dinner – always a boiling chicken, his mum bought it live and took it to the shochet to be killed. It was the cheapest option. A live chicken with its head bobbing out of his mum's shopping bag was too much for a little kid, but his pleas to keep the bird were in vain.

... After the first fall of snow even the streets of the poor looked pretty. His sister ran into the house clutching money she'd found in the snow. He said that he would also go out and find some and he did.

... As a kid he was given bits of material and a needle and cotton, to play with. He would make purses and sew buttons on shirts. He was even good at invisible mending.

3

Maple Court, 9:14 a.m.

The cigar cutter and the two badges look lost in the deep, blue velvet of the jewellery box. The badges are from two different eras: the iconic CND symbol an inspiration from the 1950s; the image of my grandmother a keepsake from the early 1900s. Now, my grandmother stares out at me. She looks so severe. She must have been only in her early twenties and she looks fifty. She had it tough.

◆

Escaping the pogroms of the Russian Empire, the young couple who would become my great-grandparents travelled first overland, then by sea, finally getting off a train at Manchester Victoria Station. Carrying all they owned in two large suitcases, they walked up the road to the Jewish quarter of Red Bank, my four year old grandmother with a cardboard sign hanging round her neck: 'RIVKA MALKOWSKI'.

I never did meet my grandmother, she, like my other grandparents had gone by the time I was born.

By the 1880s, growing numbers of working-class, Yiddish-speaking Eastern Europeans were inhabiting the streets of Hightown, Strangeways and Cheetham Hill. Hightown was poor but vibrant – exotic, even. Nearly all the streets near us were named after trees: Beech, Sycamore, Elm, Cedar. There was hardly a tree in sight. Thousands of Jewish garment workers hurried to and from the sweatshops. My aunts worked on *the donkey*, my sister was a *finisher*, my dad a *schneider*. There were a dozen synagogues, a hospital, schools, homes for the elderly, restaurants, all declaring their Jewish identity. I was happy and played out in the street until it was dark.

Being poor didn't bother me that much, until, aged eleven, I went on my first and only visit to the local wash house. I had to pay in advance for the woman in charge to run a bath. Standing in the sterile, harsh cubicle, I saw the scum mark from the last bather and thought, 'No thanks,' and went back home.

Mum said, 'Quite right. I'll talk to Rose.' At home Mum

was in charge and she knew what was right. After that, Rose Levy, who also had a television set, let me use her bath once a week.

♦

I'm supposed to take something for my sister Rita and I'm trying to remember what it is. I look at the things on the table. I haven't got a clue. I put the jewellery box in the cardboard box. Next in, is the dog-eared chocolate box with its jumble of family photographs. I hesitate. I can't resist looking at them.

♦

The one on top is my class at junior school. Teddy Jackson is in the front row, holding a wooden sign that reads *Standard 1, 1949*. Thirty-one kids, the usual suspects looking like they've just had a fight, and others all scrubbed clean and Brylcreemed.

On my way to junior school, I remember walking behind the school bully, Keith Delaney. For some reason that morning he was unable to control his bowels. Years later, confronted by a group of *yoks* out to beat me up, Delaney, their leader, put his face so close to mine, I could see large blackheads around his nose. Sneering, he said, 'We're gonna do you Malkowski.'

I whispered in his ear, reminding him of his accident on the way to school. Delaney shocked, fell back and said, 'Go on, fuck off,' and let me go.

He was a big lad. In the school photograph he's a head taller than all the other kids.

There's a nice picture of Mum and Dad all dressed up, must've been a wedding or something. And one of me, sixteen, posing in the Derby Street Ice Palace, flying high, cultivating a Tony Curtis quiff with my sister's curling tongs. It was exciting watching World Ice Dance Champion, Lawrence Demmy, practising with Jean Westwood. But not as thrilling as finally getting off with those girls from Middleton – kissing Maureen Wilson in her fluffy angora top and tiny skating skirt.

A black and white snap of Helen and me was taken in the grounds at Baguley. Baguley. Now that's the one that always gets to me. Soon after leaving school, I became infected with tuberculosis and spent six months in Baguley Sanatorium outside Manchester. It changed my life. I learnt to cope with loneliness, grew to hate routine and knew my life would be different if I came out.

I say 'if I came out', because the evening I was admitted to Baguley, Irish Kenny, one of the patients, popped into my uninviting single room, introduced himself and told me he'd been there for ten years. His soft sing-song voice painted a grim picture. 'I've got a hole in me back as big as a dinner plate. You can get it anywhere you know, the old TB. Did you know them ancient Egyptians had it?' I didn't, but from then on I kept a diary, noting how long I expected to be in, marking it up for the whole of 1958, the year ahead. In fact, Baguley turned out to be a surprisingly positive experience.

Helen, an extremely attractive forty year old in charge of the hospital library trolley, took a shine to me. She had a degree in English Literature and was determined to rescue me from ignorance. I was always a reader but I became a voracious one when bedridden. It was Helen who became my guide to contemporary literature. Not only did she suggest what I should read but she went so far as to place the books in my hands: Nabokov, Ayn Rand, James Baldwin, Patricia Highsmith, Hemingway ... They all became my bedside companions. Helen mainly went for fairly recent fiction. I read everything she threw at me, and more. I became addicted to the Bond novels. Who didn't want to be James Bond?

Later, filling in some official form or other, I would hesitate before putting TB as a past illness but soon I was glad to acknowledge it and talk about it. I knew some people felt ashamed of having had TB. I didn't. It had a powerful life affirming effect on me. I felt proud of the fact that I had overcome this serious illness. It gave me confidence that I could deal with any challenges that lay ahead.

Even so, I would never, ever stop checking my spit for any signs of blood.

Not long after Baguley I met up with one of my pals. We were reminiscing when suddenly the lad looked at me and said, 'You've changed. What's happened, you seem different?' I knew what he meant. It was true. I did feel different.

4

Maple Court, 9:18 a.m.

I put the chocolate box into the cardboard box. Boxes in boxes!

The phone rings.

'It's me, Rita.'

'I know,' I reply.

'What time you getting here?' she asks.

I glance at the clock. 'About four. I can't stay long.'

'What time's your flight?'

'Nine o'clock. Who's there?' I ask.

'Just Mum, Sophie and Cissie.'

'And the kids?'

'Of course!'

'How's Bernie?'

'He's fine. He's on overtime this week, so he's happy.' There's a pause.

'David, have you told Denise?' she asks.

'No, not yet.'

'Don't you think you should?'

'Yes, I will,' I say. 'Okay. I'm going. I haven't finished packing and I haven't got time to rabbit to you all day.'

'Charming. Go on, bugger off.' She puts the phone down.

Rita, my older, smarter sister, always holding me to account, looking out for me as long as I can remember. I wonder what she'd say if she really knew what was going on. Rita is married to Bernie and ever since the day before my sixth birthday Bernie has been my hero.

◆

It was hot, stifling hot, pitch bubble hot. When you're a kid why does the day before your birthday seem to go on forever? I was sitting on the edge of the pavement trying to pop the bubbles between the cobblestones, wondering if I would get that red fire engine with the bell, the one I'd shown Mum in Lewis's, or would I get the usual, 'something nice to wear.' I heard a noise and looked up; some men were shouting at the top of the street. Bernie was running towards me.

Earlier I'd heard Mum and Dad whispering – something

about a picture on the front page of the newspaper that Mum called a rag.

Dad said, 'They hanged two British soldiers because the British hanged three Jewish soldiers.' I didn't understand that. Or, when Dad went on, 'It's got nothing to do with us ... Jews are being attacked here, all over the place, because of something that's happening over there in Palestine. For God's sake a *shul's* been burnt down in Liverpool.'

'Keep your voice down,' Mum kept saying.

Dad took no notice of her. 'They've thrown bricks through the windows of every Jewish shop on Cheetham Hill Road. It looks like it did seven years ago, after the blitz.'

'What's the blitz?' I'd asked.

Then Mum snapped, 'Right, that's it. You go outside and play and make sure you stay in front of the house.'

So I did and that's how I got pitch on my hands.

Bernie stopped in front of me, bent down and gave me his watch. 'Take this and go back in the house,' he said quietly. Bernie didn't look Jewish and once earned pocket money as a *fire yok*, lighting fires for Jewish people on *Shabbos*.

When I got to the front door and looked back I saw him and a *goy* sizing each other up like big cats. *Bam!* Bernie punched the man in the face. Soon after that, five or six Jewish men I recognised, started fighting with other men, right there in the middle of the street.

Hightown was under attack.

♦

I suddenly remember what it is that Rita wants. *Balloon Man.*
It's on top of the record cabinet - I carefully place it between
my clothes in the suitcase. That's Rita all over. Out of all
my expensive gear the only thing she wants is a small, Royal
Doulton ceramic figurine, of an old man holding a bunch of
balloons. Mum and The Aunts don't want anything. They
don't want my fancy stuff, they're happy with what they have.

I've always been the one who wants more.

Maybe I left the world I grew up in because of surviving
TB, or meeting Wolfie, who really knows? But without having
to do very much I was catapulted into a different life.

And I'm about to move on again.

What you give up is much more than ornaments.

5

Maple Court, 9:21 a.m.

The telephone rings again. I pick it up.

'It's me again, Rita.'

'I know, and it's me again.'

'There's something wrong with you,' she says.

'I know. What do you want now?'

'Don't forget the *Balloon Man*.'

'I haven't. And I'm leaving a small box at your place,' I tell her.

She laughs and says, 'Thank you and goodbye.'

There's not much left to pack: Denise's letters, ten LPs, a book that Helen gave me, my grammar school scrapbook and a pack of cards. The scrapbook contains all my school reports, school calendar and timetable. It smells musty.

I hated the grammar school.

♦

On my first day, as I was getting off the bus, an older, bigger boy said, 'Carry my satchel,' thrusting it into my hands. I waited until we were just outside the school entrance then threw it over a hedge. During the morning's break he stopped me in the playground, threatening to punch me up but I was a mad kid and when he saw I wasn't afraid he left me alone.

One morning I went into the toilets, pulled all the toilet paper out of every cubicle, put the plugs in the sinks and turned all the taps full on. A special assembly of the whole school was called. Ronson, the Head, promised that whoever did it would be treated fairly if they owned up. I thought, *fuck you*. No chance.

In my final year, Ronson – standing on the kerb of the fireplace in his room to appear taller – threatened to beat me for something or other I'd done wrong. I was fifteen and said, 'No, you're not doing that anymore.' And he didn't.

As well as the grammar school, I used to go to the *Yeshiva* in a rambling, scruffy old house, where *frum* boys studied the *Talmud* and *Torah*. I loved the learning, poring over every word, every letter. From the outside it was a black and grey world but inside my head it was vivid, stimulating, full of colour.

Once my pal Leon Lazarus and I were at an all night gathering, studying the *Torah* on the festival of *Shavuot* which marks both the wheat harvest and the giving of the Ten Commandments at Mount Sinai. During our vigil, Leon, stretching for a biscuit across a long table, touched a hot samovar and shouted, 'Ow.'

I laughed, I was only thirteen. Leon laughed, too.

An older boy said, 'You shouldn't laugh at other people's misfortune.'

I felt put down and said to myself, 'What am I doing here? Nobody's *frum* in our house. I'm not like the other boys with sidelocks and *tzitzis* hanging over my shirt. I feel like an outsider.' It was never the same after that.

A chance event – a hot samovar – and my reluctance to fight the rising desires of puberty, were pulling me towards a different path. Much to my family's relief, I abandoned the life of a *yeshiva bocher*, got a Saturday job and found a new set of pals.

♦

I go out of the flat and I'm just about to throw the scrapbook and all its memories down the refuse chute when I stop. Shaking my head, I go back inside and put the scrapbook into the cardboard box.

6

Maple Court, 9:24 a.m.

Why keep anything? Memories? What about all that other stuff? The stuff we don't need, stuff we never look at, stuff we don't know we have. Maybe we need proof that things happened – we were there, we cared, we had a life.

The telephone rings again. It's Joseph this time. 'Well, how are you doing?' he asks.

'Nearly there, just finishing packing,' I reply.

'You can still change your mind, you know.'

'I can't, I've got to go.' It's the one thing I'm certain of.

'Okay ... Be well, David.'

'And you.' I put the phone down. I'll miss Joseph. We'd spent the last four years having a good time in the way most people only dream about.

I stack the LPs in the cardboard box. From Rosemary Clooney to Bob Dylan my few albums couldn't be more different and are too personal to give away. Denise gave me my first Dylan album when I was twenty-one.

♦

I had my twenty-first in a casino by the sea. Three of the regulars bought me presents: a bottle of champagne, a silk tie, and an Arrow shirt. The croupiers and waitresses clubbed together and gave me a tie pin with matching cufflinks.

One night, Boris Franks appeared in the Whisky A Go Go and offered me the job as dealer manager of a casino he was opening in Lytham St Annes, near Blackpool. Larger than life and never without a cigar, Boris was bald, five foot two and as round as he was tall. He was also a well-known gambler, famous for his (reputed) huge win in the Casino de Monte-Carlo.

He asked me how much I wanted to be paid.

I consulted Wolfie who said, 'Tell him to cover all your expenses and that you want a quarter of the tips.'

Boris agreed. From then on, for most of the sixties, I would earn more than the Prime Minister.

I loved the open sky, the sea air and the wild dunes of St Annes. A smart little Victorian town with a great beach, perfect for paddling, hopeless for swimming. It even had a windmill and a pier. A sedate, family resort, slotted in between the mud flats of the Ribble Estuary and the kiss-me-quick hats of Blackpool.

Boris had the idea of locating a casino in the Imperial Hotel, a majestic Edwardian icon that first opened in 1909 and claimed to be the largest seaside hotel in the country. Businessmen from Manchester, Liverpool, Leeds and other northern cities ensconced their wives and families in hotels and apartments for the summer, visiting them at weekends. Big stars appearing for the summer season in Blackpool, five miles up the never-ending coast, added to the appeal. Boris persuaded the owner of the Imperial to convert the neglected basement hydrobaths into a cocktail bar and casino. Roulette, blackjack and *chemin de fer* tables were installed, with me in charge – knowing little but learning fast. Ignorance gave me confidence.

It's amazing what girls and married women will try on a young guy dealing *chemin de fer*. I was only twenty-one and not that experienced. Hands under the table were distracting, especially when they were unsolicited and a boyfriend or husband was sitting opposite you. It was all so new: beautiful women, parties in expensive homes, meeting stars off the telly. This was a very different St Annes – a different Blackpool, too – compared with what I'd known on day trips with my dad, sitting on the seafront with packed sandwiches, or on dancing jaunts with my pals to the Winter Gardens.

Harry Rose and his girl friend Eve, on holiday from Newcastle upon Tyne, came into the casino one evening and offered to buy me a drink. We sat at the bar chatting. They asked me about how I came to be in the gambling business. Harry and his brother Joseph were opening a nightclub and were looking for an experienced casino manager. Harry suggested I came up north to meet Joseph.

I didn't know where Newcastle was but I went.

The brothers met me at the station. Harry came up to me as I got off the train and said, 'This is my brother, Joseph.' We shook hands. 'Let's go and look at the club,' Harry said.

'D'you want a coffee or something to eat first?' asked Joseph.

'I'm fine. Let's go,' I replied.

Joseph was twenty-four, tall, handsome, gentle, Spanish-looking, and he'd been educated at the best schools. Harry was in his early forties, nobody's fool, straight as a die, had left school at fourteen to work and he looked after the whole family.

Their Jaguar was parked outside the station. After a quick tour of the town, they showed me a new building on a small piece of land that their father had owned. It was in an alley in the town centre. After years in the costume jewellery business, with shops around the north-east of England, their big adventure was happening: a nightclub, Las Vegas style.

The ground floor was big enough for a five hundred seater club with a casino on the floor above. It was due to open in six months. I liked the look of it. The brothers hardly asked me anything about my gambling experience. They were more interested in where I came from, my background and family.

Afterwards they took me for dinner to Sam's Inn, a kind of steak bar, where they knew the owner who came over and made a fuss of them. Harry ordered corn on the cob as a starter. I didn't know what it was but went for it anyway. When it arrived I tried to cut it with a knife and fork. Joseph put me straight, whispering out the side of his mouth, 'Just pick it up and eat it.'

I said, 'What a shmock,' and we all started laughing.

When they asked me, just as Boris had, how much money I wanted to work for them, I followed Wolfie's advice.

They offered me the job.

Boris himself was also moving on, opening a purpose-built casino outside Manchester. He made it clear there was a job for me. But I wanted a change. My sisters were now both married with families. Sandra had two children and was living in New York. Rita, Bernie and their three kids were still in the same street we'd grown up in. Going to Newcastle meant living away from home but Rita was near Mum, which was good and I could take care of the finances. I decided to go with the Rose brothers and their new club, Copacabana. As I prepared to leave town, it was with Mum making it very clear she wasn't pleased about me being in the gambling business.

But, feeling good, I bought myself a new car, a Singer Gazelle. It was a nice car, reliable, steady, not too fast, and – it wouldn't take me long to find out – not for me. Still, the smell of a new car is hard to resist. I got behind the wheel and headed north for the Copacabana.

... Shalosh Seudos is an afternoon gathering on a Shabbos with refreshments. They would sing songs and the boy's Rabbi would treat his pupils to cucumber sandwiches and tiny squares of halva. The revered Rabbi Zilberg always joined them and they would wait until he arrived before starting. One Shabbos the boy arrived after all the other boys, just about the time Rabbi Zilberg usually came in. When the boy opened the door all the other boys stood up out of respect thinking it was the visiting Rabbi. Everybody fell about laughing when they saw who it was. The boy's Rabbi said, 'Don't laugh, one day you may all have to stand up for this boy.' He was secretly thrilled and wondered what it could mean.

7

The Big Freeze began on Boxing Day 1962 and went on for nearly three months.

Ray was moaning. 'How cold is this place and how fucking long is this snow going to last?'

We were carefully navigating the mounds of dirty grey frozen ice and snow that had been lying on the pavement outside our flat for over two months.

'I don't understand a word anybody says and after ten o'clock this town turns into the Wild West,' he grumbled. Ray wasn't too enamoured with Newcastle, and it didn't help that we had moved there in the middle of the worst winter for two hundred years. It was the coldest place either of us had ever been.

Ray and I had been pals since we were croupiers together at the Whisky A Go Go. I had lined him up for a job in the Copacabana casino. For a Jewish boy and a Caribbean boy to have become friends was unusual. In fact I'd never met a black person until I got to know Ray. He was my age but his slicked-back black hair gave him an older, 1930s movie star appearance. He wore shades *all* the time. A mean trumpet player, he'd quickly got the measure of the music scene, dragging me to hear the best of jazz, rhythm and blues: Errol Garner, The Animals, Sonny Boy Williamson. It wasn't *exactly* wasted on me, but I was the guy that spent the evening chatting to Brian Epstein instead of talking to The Beatles.

I liked Newcastle upon Tyne, though: its closeness to the river, the bold bridges crossing the Tyne, its strong character, brisk air; the people chatty and friendly. I liked the city. Grey Street and Eldon Square were grand and there were lots of impressive buildings, even if they had become blackened with industrial grime. It felt an optimistic place to be, despite the steady decline of its major industries, coal mining and ship building. Undeterred by high unemployment, Geordies celebrated, especially at the weekend and Copacabana was one of a dozen successful nightclubs in the city centre. On the coldest of nights the lads and girls would be out on the town, no jackets, short sleeves, skirts up to their bums. Newcastle was its own land, with its own people and language. It was like being in a foreign country and that appealed to me. I knew I was going to do all right.

Ray needed more and I knew he wasn't going to last very long. He didn't. I was sorry to see him go, but I stayed. It was different for me – earning a lot of money, running things, enjoying the anonymity of living in a strange new city. And Copacabana, for a short time, became one of the most famous nightclubs in the country. The Rose brothers brought the biggest stars of the day to Newcastle: Tommy Cooper, Matt Munro, Alma Cogan, a host of American singers and cabaret acts, Billy Daniels, Mel Tormé, Jayne Mansfield, and even former World Heavyweight Champion Joe Louis. Like my days on the markets, when I would stand by the side of market stalls watching the best spielers pull and work a crowd, now I stood by the stage, night after night, watching the best acts in the business weave their magic on the audience.

Whenever celebrities were in town they would drop in. I met Ray Charles, Shirley Bassey, Tom Jones. It was the place to be, with two resident house bands, a glass dance floor and chicken in the basket. What more could you want? The club was full, the casino was raking it in. I was living the high life. I'd changed my name as soon as I arrived in Newcastle, going as David Mall. I wonder now, if deep down I was ashamed of being in the gambling business, bothered that even from a distance Mum was still on my case. But back then, it was the swinging sixties. I was twenty-two and I was on top. The Singer Gazelle was long gone, replaced by a series of Jags, then Mercedes.

I had made it.

Harry and Joseph Rose were both *mensches*. They never

spoke ill of other people and were much liked. The three of us got on really well, had a similar sense of humour and worked hard. Both of them were in the club every night except for the odd occasion when they had a break. Harry went to Italy for a two-week holiday with Eve. For the first three days he rang the club each night – then came back. He couldn't handle sitting on a beach wondering what was going on with the business. It probably wasn't as much fun being on holiday as it was at work. Joseph was more relaxed about it all. Sought after by beautiful women, he would take off to glamorous places.

Firing elastic bands carefully placed on the tip of the first finger is an acquired skill. Much to Harry's irritation Joseph and I were good at it. The office was our practice range. When the targets were photographs of him posing with stars, he would go mad and say, 'It's disrespectful', which would send Joseph and me into hysterics.

I moved out of the modest flat Ray and I had been sharing into Maple Court, a smart new apartment block in Whitley Bay. It was the first time I'd had somewhere to live that I could furnish to my own taste. I relished it. Whitley Bay, a sleepy seaside town eight miles from Newcastle suited me. From the lounge window I could see St Mary's Lighthouse to the north and to the south, Tynemouth's derelict Castle and Priory. Like so many English seaside resorts it was at the end of its glory days. The donkey rides, beach huts and countless seaside cafes a thing of the past. The 'North East's Blackpool', now offered the Spanish City - an ornate run-down funfair at one end of town, a few novelty shops and ice cream parlours, scattered along the expansive promenade, a depleted number of B&Bs and a few sad-looking, once grand, Victorian hotels.

Everything changes. I was mooching in an antique shop on the seafront and came across a postcard of Wilhelmina, the mechanical elephant who had had a full-time job transporting adults and kids up and down the once-crowded beach. Poor Wilhelmina, like her many brothers and sisters dotted around the country's fading seaside towns, she was now rusting away in a warehouse, hoping one day to make a comeback. Whitley Bay did still have a great beach, not that I ever sat on it much. I liked it best in winter when the hardy few battled the gales and the raging North Sea challenged anybody to get too close.

Mrs Henderson sort of came with the flat. She'd been the previous occupant's housekeeper and I was only too happy to keep her on. I didn't have to do any cleaning, shopping, washing, ironing or make my own breakfast for the foreseeable future. She was a lovely, sprightly, curly-haired lady in her early fifties, who looked after me like I was her son.

It's surprising how quickly you get used to big money, even when you haven't had it before. I bought expensive watches, rings and cufflinks. I had jewellery made to my own design. Manchester tailor, Harry Stoller, made my suits from beautiful Reid and Taylor cloth, sewn by hand by Frankie Kravitz, sitting cross-legged on a table, inches away from the bare light bulb. I loved the moment when the tacked-in sleeves were pulled out, a far cry from the days when I wore Gerald's jacket. Gerald, my older cousin, was a small man in his late thirties when I was only ten and even if my mum did take up the sleeves, the jacket length made it obvious that I was a boy wearing a man's jacket. I came top of the year in my junior school and all I could think of, as I went up before the whole school to collect my prize, was the stupid, fucking long jacket I was wearing.

That was then. Now I was in the money, living on the coast, with a housekeeper and too many suits to count. It had all happened so fast. It was not my doing. I didn't have a plan. I had made choices but only after chance had opened the doors. I was living in a bubble, working and playing in the city centre, driving my big car from my swish flat to the club and back home again. I was a night worker. I got up late, had plenty of time to relax before work, finished when the club closed around two in the morning or later if the casino was busy. Occasionally I caught a glimpse of the other world, the drab, colourless world, the overcrowded back streets of Newcastle's East End, women pushing prams full of laundry to the wash house, fag-smoking young blokes looking twice their age, scruffy, snotty-nosed kids.

It took me back. Newcastle upon Tyne in the early 1960s was like Hightown in Manchester – the people were great, the living conditions, grim.

8

Maple Court, 9:35 a.m.

I need to put something else into the cardboard box. There's too much space. Maybe something soft. I know – my trilby. Only ever used for funerals and going to *shul*. It's perfect. I was going to throw it away. I bought it back then - in the other life.

◆

With only a bare light bulb in the scullery kitchen, it was almost impossible to shave in the postcard-size mirror that hung on a nail above the mangle. Getting ready to go out wasn't much fun. It was dark, damp, and the distemper on the walls came off on your clothes. A night out usually entailed dancing at the Ritz, jazz concerts at the Free Trade Hall, very occasionally a Chinese at the Ping Hong on Oxford Road, or maybe a spaghetti bolognese in one of the newly-opened coffee bars. Sometimes, a few of the lads, with girls, would go to a dull dinner dance at a posh hotel in Prestbury for an evening of warm music, warm duck *à l'orange*, and a warm bottle of Sauterne. If you got lucky you could finish up staying the night.

I was a Manchester boy and proud of it. Liverpool and Leeds up the road didn't count, calling Birmingham the second city was a joke and London had a tip about itself. A tough, no nonsense, war-scarred city, long past its heyday as *Cottonopolis* and the beating heart of the industrial revolution, Manchester was real, cocky and for good measure had some magnificent buildings.

My first proper job was with Holmes Terry, a wholesale drapers in the city centre. I went into the staff toilet one day and finding no soap to wash my hands went into the managers' toilet. I was reported to the Managing Director who asked me why I'd done it. I explained and he said, 'That's a good reason, but you're fired.'

Enough of straight jobs, I thought. I'd been working on the markets on Saturdays and decided to do it full time. I loved it, out in the fresh air, free as a bird, fun, and a van to drive. My new boss sold bedding, a brilliant pitcher, adept at pulling and entertaining the crowd: 'Missus, come forward and smell the flowers on this candlewick bedspread ... move your legs your body will follow.' They'd laugh and do exactly as he asked. Talk about street theatre, he was the best turn in town. I would practise for hours in front of the mirror, itching to try it for real and at the same time scared stiff. The first time I tried it was the last. I was hopeless.

Abnormality seemed to be the norm and colourful characters were everywhere. We worked Moss Side market on a Saturday and the guy who ran it insisted the stall rent had to be given to him in a sealed envelope. He would hold it to his ear, shake it vigorously and pretending it was a watch declare, 'Leave it to me, I'll get it fixed.' He performed this charade without fail every week.

The streets were no less crazy. Difficult to top was Mrs Pavlovsky who lived two doors up. Sammy Gordon sold green groceries from a horse and cart. I was behind Mrs P and her eight year old son Alexi, when she produced a brown paper bag full of something. She handed it to Sammy saying, '*Vzves gryaz.*' Sammy, who didn't speak Russian, asked Mrs P what she was on about.

Mrs P nudged Alexi, who sheepishly told Sammy that his mother had said, 'Weigh the dirt.' Alexi looked round at me, sniggered, then said to Sammy, 'Mum says she won't pay for the dirt on the potatoes she's just bought. She wants you to weigh it and give her some money back.'

Sammy nodded slowly a few times, then very carefully gave Alexi some money and said, 'Do me a favour sonny, tell your mother to start growing her own potatoes.'

My mother laughed when I told her the story. 'What do you expect from Russian boots,' she muttered.

It seemed Mrs Pavlovsky still wore the same boots she had on when she'd first arrived from Omsk.

♦

I go into the bedroom, get the trilby, try it on and look at myself in the mirror. I'm not sure I like what I see.

I squeeze it into the cardboard box. It's just right.

♦

I once kept a trilby, glasses and a raincoat in a small Ford Thames van I'd bought (and which, Dad claimed, proved I had big ideas). I met Angela at the Ritz, a really nice girl, about five years older than me, relatively posh, looked like Grace Kelly. We went out for a little while. She lived in a fancy house in Buxton and stayed with her Auntie Jean in Manchester during the week. Auntie Jean was stone deaf and Angela used to let me back in after I'd loudly said goodnight. Wearing my disguise (trilby, glasses, raincoat), I would sneak in, then out again in the morning. A bit risky, but ...

Not as theatrical as Danny Marcus. There were thousands of GIs stationed twenty miles away in Burtonwood Air Base and in the 1950s it was not unusual to see American airmen in the pubs and dance halls at the weekend. Danny used to dress up as a GI to get the girls. Once I was on the Ritz balcony when I heard a loud American-sounding, 'Ha ha.' It was Danny in full GI uniform, sitting at a table, showing a girl photographs of his non-existent Cadillac and luxury home in California. As I walked past him he exclaimed, 'Hi, Dave, good to see you man, stay cool.' I looked at him and thought, *you plonker.*

I ran into Danny years later when he was a theatrical agent, still posing as an American.

All this craziness was of another world, different to the straight, normal one out there.

9

Maple Court, 9:40 a.m.

Denise's love letters, laid out before me on the table, sit in silent testimony to how much I screwed up.

Reading old love letters, even if they are for you, is like looking at somebody else's diary. They're private, especially if they say, 'destroy after reading'. Her words, interspersed with drawings, are funny, loving and full of hope for us. Denise didn't hold back and neither did I. We declared our love and at the same time struggled with wanting to retain our independence. I'm not sure why.

♦

I first saw her in the Whisky A Go Go. She was with another girl, a friend from college, and they came over to the chemmy table to watch. I was dealing, yet I couldn't take my eyes off her. I signalled Ray to take over. I had to talk to her. Trying to be cool I went up to her and said, 'Are you a big time gambler, then?'

She deliberately, slowly, looked me up and down and said, 'No, but I'm prepared to take a chance.'

We both started laughing and that was it.

Everything about Denise White was different from other girls I knew. She was only eighteen and lived in Stockport, near Manchester, with her mother – her father was dead. I felt protective towards her. She was just lovely. She had a beautiful smile and when she looked at you she wasn't looking anywhere else. She was innocent and sexy, a red-haired Pre-Raphaelite, Celtic beauty with arched eyebrows, freckled skin and bruised lips. She was training to be a dancer.

We became friends, couldn't see enough of each other, and decided to go on holiday together. Denise was strong-willed. Actually it was her idea to go on holiday and there was no need to question it. Neither of us had been abroad or flown before and when the plane was caught in a thunderstorm we were terrified – compounded by the sight of two nuns in front praying, babies crying, and the woman across the aisle constantly crossing herself and repeatedly saying, *'Por favor, por favor, por favor.'*

We made it. We landed in the late afternoon in the unforgettable balmy heat of Las Palmas basking in Gran

Canaria's Atlantic Ocean ninety miles off the coast of the Western Sahara. The sky was blue and cloudless, a hotel taxi was waiting for us, and like two kids we sat in the back pointing out the palm trees, donkeys and glistening beaches. After an hour we drove into a lush park and stopped in front of what looked like an oriental palace, The Hotel Santa Catalina. Our room was splendid. It had a veranda overlooking a tropical garden, marble floors scattered with exotic carpets and beneath an ornate carved wooden headboard, the biggest bed imaginable. In the centre of the bathroom was a large old-fashioned roll top bath with claw feet, crowned with enormous chrome taps and a bizarre-looking shower contraption. There were enough towels to open a market stall, plus two plush bath robes and slippers. The man at Thomas Cook was right. 'It's palatial,' he'd promised.

Apart from my newly-purchased holiday gear, I'd brought a pack of cards, *The Ipcress File*, and a last minute buy at the airport, *The Hidden Persuaders*. Denise had something called *My Life* about the dancer Isadora Duncan, another book, *Girl With Green Eyes*, a drawing pad, and *Scrabble*. She had a fair few clothes and sun cream, which I'd forgotten to bring. Straightaway we showered, got changed and headed for the bar to order the first of what became our holiday drink – champagne cocktails. Dinner wasn't for two hours so we took a stroll round the gardens. The luxury of wearing summer clothes in December, having nothing to do for the next two weeks, giddy from the cocktails – bliss.

The dining room was a treat, too: chandeliers, exquisitely laid tables, lit candles and a superb à la carte menu. That suited me. I had an aversion to set menus and buffets – especially buffets. Unlike at home, the waiters were young, attentive, polite and seemed to be enjoying the job. We ate simply, had another champagne cocktail and then went back to the room.

We made love for the first time, naturally, easily. It felt right. Denise was passionate, adventurous yet innocent, exciting. We stayed in bed, had breakfast in the room, made love again and managed to get out by noon. This, more or less, was our pattern for the next two weeks. Occasionally, we made it to the local beach but more often we hung out in cafes watching the action. For part of the day it was usually cloudy because of the trade winds which made it that much more pleasant to sit around or walk into town. Best of all, was sitting on the veranda reading, lying on the bed, playing Scrabble or poker, arguing over the couple of books we had to share, making love. Denise sketched, I took photographs. It was idyllic.

She was three years younger than I was. It could have been a generation. It wasn't that my life had been that dissimilar from hers, we were just different that's all, but we got on. She dressed down not up. She watched ballet. I watched boxing. I bought her jewellery, perfume and clothes, she bought me books, records and toys, but we got on.

Sometime later, Denise and I were together when President Kennedy was assassinated. Denise couldn't stop crying. 'What a terrible, terrible thing to happen,' she sobbed. 'He was a beacon of hope, a man of integrity and honour.'

I agreed and said, 'It is terrible and he did seem to be special, but he was only a man, an avid James Bond fan who'd had a string of affairs.'

She went mad and wouldn't speak to me for two hours.

Denise was the most positive person I'd ever met. She was kind. Driven by a strong moral code she would challenge any injustices she came across. If she didn't have her head in a book, she was drawing. At her instigation we would go to art galleries and the theatre. She dressed like a gypsy and embraced the day as a free spirit. She was always fun to be with. We talked about love but we were living separate lives in different places, not wanting to be tied down. We gave each other space, we were free agents on a fast moving track and these were changing times.

Still, we saw each other regularly, meeting in London or Manchester. Sometimes she would come with me to see my mother. They got on really well, particularly as neither of them were impressed by the gambling business and *never* stopped reminding me I was capable of better things.

Denise asked me to go and see her end of year dance performance. I hadn't seen her perform before and after checking into a hotel in Kensington I got a cab to the college, a large house somewhere in West London. It reminded me of the *Yeshiva* but not as scruffy. It was early summer, a warm evening, lots of parents and excited students, a rarefied atmosphere and although I felt out of place, I liked it.

Denise had told me what to expect: 'All girls, dancing together in groups, in pairs or on their own. It's modern dance, just relax and enjoy it.' I did enjoy it but found it too melodramatic and repetitive, without really understanding what it was about. When Denise danced it was different, though. She performed on her own to a piece of classical music which she told me later was the *Adagio from Bach's Violin Sonata No.1 in G Minor.* She became a vision in a white diaphanous dress, moving freely, a lyrical, acrobatic accompaniment to the haunting music. Music new to my ears. I was held in suspension as if holding my breath.

Afterwards we went to a French brasserie nearby. I told her how much I loved her dancing and that it actually aroused me, which was true. A good-looking guy came up to our table and told Denise how much he enjoyed her solo and what a wonderful dancer she was. Denise flushed, she often did, and thanked him. When he had left I said, 'That guy really fancied you.' We laughed. The conversation turned to being attracted to other people.

Denise said, 'The trouble with most relationships is that they are too closed and need to be more open.' She did a strange thing. She took a pad out of her bag, drew two vertical lines alongside each other which halfway down the page branched out to the left and right then came together again and continued down the page. 'That's you and me,' she said. 'We may go off and do other things, meet other people, but we'll always come back to each other.'

I kept thinking about what she'd said and why she'd said it.

Two weeks later I met Cathy.

... His favourite story was the one his Rabbi told, about a boy who was at home reading, his father upstairs sleeping. A man came to the house to speak to the boy's father. He told the boy he had come to buy a carpet and needed to pick it up that day. The boy told the man his father was sleeping and he didn't want to wake him. The man said he would come back in half an hour and left a note stating the amount he wished to offer for the carpet. The man came back three times, but the boy wouldn't wake his father who was still sleeping. Every time the man increased his offer. Finally his father woke up. The man laughed on seeing the boy's father, commenting on what a clever ruse it was to get more money for the carpet. The boy's father told the man that it wasn't a ruse and accepted his first offer.

10

Ella and Marty, a couple I am friendly with, are taking over the flat and have bought all my furniture. I suppose I should leave them a note. I look for something to write with. I still have my Asprey leather note pad with gold corners and a gold Cross pen. I'll give them to Bernie seeing as I'm obviously determined to get rid of any reminders of wealth.

Bernie won't want them either, though. I know that.

The phone rings for the fourth time. It's George.

'I hear you're leaving town,' he says.

'That's right. Where are you?' I ask warily.

'I'm here, I was expecting to see you this weekend.' He pauses, but I haven't said anything. 'This all seems a bit sudden, David. I spoke to Cathy and she's very upset. Why don't we meet and talk about it?' George's voice is soft and persuasive.

Cathy will have told George everything. 'I can't talk now but we can meet later. What about three o'clock in the Turk's Head bar?' I lie.

He says, 'Oh, the Turk's Head. Okay, see you at three,' and rings off.

I can tell George is surprised I suggested meeting somewhere public. I look at myself in the hall mirror, despairing over my stupidity. I say out loud, 'You fucking shmock,' and shake my head, remembering how not so long ago I'd been riding the wave.

11

I picked up a copy of *Time* magazine on the way into London. The Supremes, the ultimate club act, were on the front cover. They were booked for the Copacabana ... New York not Newcastle!

I was looking in the mirror shaving, in a suite at the May Fair Hotel – twelve guineas a night; nothing to me. Why shouldn't I be enjoying the quiet luxury, flowers and fruit in the room, waiting for a selection of shirts from the nearby gent's outfitters? Then, later, a cup of tea in the back room of Billy Queen's betting shop on Park Lane, followed by an evening at the Victoria Sporting Club. I shook my head. At times it was still hard to believe that I was the casino manager of one of the most successful nightclubs in the country.

If there was time, I thought, I'd pick up cigars. I'd developed a taste for Cuban Romeo y Julieta, bought in boxes of twenty-five from Fribourg & Treyer of Piccadilly where the shop walls were lined with wooden humidors and the shop assistants wore morning suits. The cedar boxes had a sliding top, occasionally hinged, always with a paper-thin cedar cover resting on top of the cigars. I loved the way the shop assistants brought out bundles of cigars tied with red ribbon, for me to feel and smell. I had quickly learned that when gently rolled between my fingers they should have a little give, not feel too dry and never smell stale or of mould.

My mind flicked back to the evening's entertainment. By now I knew something about gambling that only gamblers know. The excitement, the anticipation, the feeling of uncertainty that makes your guts twist. Like getting ready to meet a girl you really fancy for the first time. Only better.

Whenever I came to London I played chemmy. Given that it's purely a game of chance, my strategy was simple: when out of luck play tight, when in luck play it up. Five-card stud poker was my other game of choice and that required skill.

I finished shaving and took a final look in the mirror. Yes. I was certainly ready to gamble – just not yet aware that it would turn out to be for far more than money.

I was carrying a fair amount – a thousand pounds in cash – when I entered the Victoria Sporting Club at nine that night. 'The Vic' was a vast, opulent sea of green, red and gold, lit by glittering sputnik chandeliers. A wealthy free-for-all: roulette, dice and blackjack tables, roped off areas for poker and chemmy, croupiers standing around waiting for action, French dining, flashy men with young women, the familiar casino hum of roulette balls clicking and excited dice players calling bets, winners laughing and losers crying all the way home. Of all the London casinos I'd tried, from stuffy Crockfords to the gimmicky Playboy, it was the Victoria I liked best. It was friendly.

I was there to play, not play around, but that night it didn't go according to plan. The chemmy game wasn't quite ready to start. I wandered over to a roulette table, a game I rarely played. I noticed the croupier, picking up on her Geordie accent. She smiled at me. I was confident, I knew women found me attractive and the money helped. She was a tall girl with long blonde hair, wearing a pink sparkly beaded top. Her blue eyes, pale skin and defiant look attracted me, made her seem both vulnerable and hard. She was probably a bit older than me. I thought, *maybe it's my lucky night.*

I was twenty-three, so I put a couple of five pound notes on twenty-three. She exchanged the notes for a house chip and spun the ball and wheel in opposite directions. We watched as the ball jumped and rattled around the spinning wheel, bouncing off the diamond-shaped deflectors set above the numbers, until it landed into one of the thirty-seven pockets. She called out, 'Twenty-three red.' Then she paid me out at 35 to 1, six fifty pound chips, two twenties and a ten, plus my original stake, and smiled again.

I gave her a twenty pound chip. 'What time do you

finish?' I asked, smiling in return.

She looked at the tip, nodded appreciatively and put it in a slot on the table. 'Thanks. I break in ten minutes. I'm back on again at ten.'

'Why don't you ask Charles to let you go?' I said casually. Charles was the floor supervisor and I was a well-known face. We were on nodding terms.

'Who shall I say is trying to kidnap me?'

I laughed. 'Tell him it's David and I promise to have you in bed by midnight.'

'Can't wait,' she fired back, and walked over to Charles.

I followed her long legs, like an exotic bird gliding across the floor, her head tilted slightly to one side. My easy banter would be no match for her dominant sexuality.

She kissed me as soon as we got in the taxi and told me her name was Cathy. I'd read about La Trattoria Terrazza in Soho, an Italian restaurant Frank Sinatra was seen in recently.

I suggested that's where we go to eat. There was a long queue, lots of people milling around, an over-large sky-blue Rolls badly parked outside. I went to the front of the queue and spoke to the doorman, quietly offering him five pounds. In a loud voice he announced, 'Yes we do have your booking sir, please follow me.' I gestured to Cathy and we went in.

We were about to be seated at a table I didn't like, I whispered to the waiter, who moved us to a much better table by the wall, beside a huge mirror, reflecting the other diners.

It was busy and felt expectant, as if a show was about to start. Cathy couldn't hide her excitement when she leaned over to me, and said, 'Gregory Peck is sitting behind you in the corner.'

I nodded. I certainly wasn't going to turn round. The waiters were wearing long sleeved T-shirts, with horizontal blue and white stripes and looked like sailors. The food was fantastic but we were both in a hurry.

♦

I couldn't get enough of her. I was drunk on her earthy smell. Eventually we fell into a deep sleep wrapped around each other.

Late morning we ordered coffee, toast, and Mediterranean prawns served in the centre of a chrome platter surrounded by crushed ice. Then Cathy left and I caught the afternoon flight home. On the plane, the thing I clearly remembered was that when we'd gone back to the May Fair Hotel the young lad on reception suggested Cathy should sign in. She jumped at him and said she was my secretary and that she was there to work and anyway it had nothing to do with him. He flushed and didn't reply. Cathy, pushing it, said, 'And while you're at it send up a bottle of champagne and two glasses.'

She rang me six weeks later. She said she thought she was pregnant and would need a hundred pounds for an abortion.

I felt afraid. The only thing I could think of was to say I would send her the money. She said no. She wanted to see me and would come to Newcastle.

I put the phone down and stood in the hallway not sure what to do. After a minute I went into the lounge, sat in the rocker, got up and stared out the window. It was raining. I was supposed to take the car in for a service. On the way to the garage all I could think about was how to tell Denise. What could I say to her? What would she say? Would this affect our relationship?

... When the boy was fifteen he knew he was in love with his cousin, a beautiful girl - his age to the day. She told him, 'If you don't like somebody don't become their lover.' She had already kissed him on the mouth and said if he wanted to touch her breasts he could and that she wanted to touch him. They arranged to see each other that weekend. It was not to be. By Thursday he was trapped with his mother and father, sister and two brothers on a train slowly travelling East.

12

I didn't know what to expect. I wasn't looking forward to it.

I picked up Cathy at the train station. She looked stunning, like a model. I was aware that I didn't know much about her other than that she was a Geordie and had family on Tyneside. The last time we met we hadn't spoken much. I had this feeling in my gut and didn't know if I was still afraid or excited. I wanted to have sex with her but wasn't sure if I liked her. As soon as she got in the car she lit a cigarette, smiled and said, 'So, how are you?'

I said, 'I'm fine. More to the point, how are you?'

She laughed and casually said, 'False alarm, I'm not pregnant and I don't need your money.'

Despite my overwhelming relief, I couldn't help thinking I'd been put through some sort of test. As soon as we got to my place we went to bed.

I was due in work at eight o'clock that evening and asked

her if she wanted to come in with me. She said she was going to see her mother who lived in Gateshead, across the Tyne, but would come to the club later that night.

Saturday night was always a big game and I would be dealing in the chemmy room. The regular faces were there: Ike Goldman, Tommy Rea, Bing Ji, Alec Glock and at least a dozen other big players, nearly all wealthy business men who loved to gamble.

Matt Munro was on in the cabaret room and the club was packed. He'd become an international star with songs like "My Kind of Girl" and "Walk Away". Matt's show was due to come down at ten o'clock and that's when the casino would fill up and the chemmy start. Whenever a big star was on there would always be new faces as well as the regulars.

I went into the chemmy room to check all was in order. The chemmy table dominated the room, with nine comfortable black leather chairs round the table, plus a croupier's high chair. Sitting on the green baize was the shoe, six sealed packs of cards and the croupier's palette – a long flat wooden stick for moving the cards and chips around. On the croupier's left was a slot for tips, on the right a slot for the house fee paid by the players, and slightly off centre, a slot for the cards used during each round. Over the chemmy table were two large gold-fringed lampshades, giving a soft light for the play. The walls were covered in expensive wallpaper, embossed, dark red velour and the carpet matched the wallpaper. The door leading in and out of the main casino was padded, buttoned, black leather. The room smelt of cigars and coffee.

I fitted right in. I took great care over my appearance. That night I was wearing a dark charcoal mohair dinner suit, a white Le Roi voile dress shirt with a black self-tie bow and Bally shoes. My cufflinks were patterned gold half spheres and I had on a gold Bueche Girod dress watch, my favourite. I carried few keys (they spoiled the line of my jacket) but always a small gold cigar cutter and in my inside jacket pocket, a brown leather case containing two cigars.

I was ready, it was time; the players were coming in. I could feel the excitement.

Once they were all seated, I offered the players the six sealed decks to open and shuffle. Often they left it up to me, they were too busy chatting to each other. After shuffling the cards I asked the player to my left to cut them. I then brought all the cards together and inserted a plain black card about ten cards from the end of the packs – when this appears it indicates that the current hand is the last one before a new shuffle. Next I placed the six decks in the shoe, with their backs facing out. As in many casinos in the early days, the decks used were Waddingtons Number 1, a brand first introduced in the late 1930's. They came in red and blue backs. For variation we used three of each colour.

The thing I've always loved about playing cards is their brilliant design, palm-sized for convenient handling, a superb example of symmetry. You can't pick up a card the wrong way. The pips denoting the suits are arranged centrally and again under the numbers, whichever way up you hold a card, you can instantly tell its value and suit. It even applies to the image on the court cards which are designed with reverse symmetry. The backs of the Waddingtons are covered in symbols similar to hawthorn florets, arranged in a symmetrical formation of nine columns and sixteen rows, surrounded by a scroll motif border. We love symmetry. It represents order and makes us feel safe and secure.

As a dealer, I was fast, always polite, rarely took a break and sometimes dealt for four or five hours at a stretch. Chemmy was played at the most twice a week and on the other nights I watched the tables in the main casino and occasionally, to keep my hand in, dealt blackjack.

I've dealt and played *chemin de fer* for hundreds of nights and thousands of hours. I've watched people win fortunes and lose everything. It's a game of chance with little or no skill involved. However, invariably there are patterns that emerge during the course of an evening. Call it form, call it luck, but bet against somebody in form and you run the risk of blowing your money. We usually attribute form to games of skill like tennis or snooker and we talk about how this or that player is in form, playing well, maximising their skill. My observation of good chemmy players is that when they spot someone in form – having a good run, they avoid betting against them and when they realise they themselves are in form they will let their money ride to try and capitalise on it.

I learned that gamblers come in all shapes, sizes and guises. I've seen clever people throw childish tantrums and mild-mannered elderly men turn into kicking, screaming yobs. I've been physically attacked by a respectable man and his wife for calling the final spin on a roulette table. I've had to stop a drunken boxer from betting when he had no money. I've had to shield a doctor hiding under a chemmy table to avoid being seen by his irate wife. One night I was dealing when a young woman came over to this guy playing chemmy, whispered in his ear and left. He saw me looking and said, 'We got married today and she's a bit pissed off with me.' He carried on playing until the morning.

What amateurs have in common, is that they love to tell you about the night they won a pile of money, rarely talk about their losses, never think they play badly and are always unlucky when they lose. They play for different reasons and unlike professionals, their actions range from extreme caution to total recklessness. They're there because of the glamour, the social interaction, it makes them feel important. Hooked on risk, often chasing losses, they gamble to escape the mundane, their responsibilities, the outside world – even time. Winning is up there, but not as much as fantasizing about what they will do with their winnings. And they get the biggest high of all from a delusion: they believe they possess the power to control chance.

Professionals earn a living by gambling. They play to feed the family and to pay the bills. They play the odds, watch the other players, quit if they're playing badly, try to minimise their losses and maximise their winnings. When they play, they're fresh, they've been relaxing all day and don't have to get up for work the next morning. I liked to think I could become a member of this tribe. I studied the few books available on gambling, especially poker. I gained some knowledge of the mathematical probabilities of playing and winning but I was well aware that there were other factors at play, psychological and emotional, that all too often determine how you play and whether you win or lose.

Experience, practice and skill enable professional card players to make on the spot winning decisions. However, should they have a lapse of concentration, let their opponent off the hook, boost their opponent's confidence in any way, they may find themselves sitting in a chair all night watching the other players clean up. Players and pundits often say the cards never forgive. Poor play and missed opportunities can lead to a dramatic turn around in the fortune of gamblers but this is not due to the revenge of inanimate objects such as a deck of cards. It's just down to careless play and a careless player suffering from a serious lapse of concentration.

Then there's luck, which is supposed to even out over the long term. However, should it choose to make an appearance at the right time for you, then all bets are off and even if you are an amateur you may need a suitcase to carry off your winnings. The caveat, however, is that an amateur who plays long enough will always finish up with an empty suitcase.

On that particular night, Alec Glock called six winning bets as a punter and won every one, carrying off about two hundred pounds. Alec was a big man, a careful man, probably in his late sixties. He would methodically remove the elastic bands from around bundles of notes and put them in his pocket for later use. When it came to his turn as the banker he put in fifty pounds, a lot for a starting bank. He not only finished up doing a six-timer but he let it all ride every time. He wasn't always covered to the max but he did win more than two and a half grand. Before the night was over he had three more winning banks which again he let ride each time, withdrawing most of his winnings just at the right time. On three occasions the punters had eight against him, more often than not a winning hand, but each time Alec turned over a nine and won. A man in form. Only problem? He was a lousy tipper.

Ike Goldman, who was doing his brains in, kept betting against Alec, losing even more money. And when Ike one time had a fantastic winning bank, instead of letting it all ride he kept pulling money out of the bank, winning peanuts compared to what he should have won. Man out of form. In hindsight it's easy to say he played badly, but when you've been losing all night there's a tendency to pull up the drawbridge.

Malky Davies as usual appeared very late. Malky had a restaurant out of town and came loaded with the takings. He didn't hold back in his betting and seemed determined to blow all his money as fast as possible. He never sat down. He would bet as a punter, pacing up and down behind the seated players, calling *banco* – the whole amount in the bank – regardless of how much it was. It was no different that night and within minutes he was losing a couple of grand. Then out of nowhere he finished up in an altercation with Tommy Rea. Before I knew it they were fighting – well, not really, more like trying to slap each other. It seems Malky owed Tommy money and Tommy objected to Malky calling bets when he hadn't been paid yet. As they were both unfit, elderly men it soon stopped. Needless to say, the kibbitzers had a field day saying stuff like, 'What round is this? I didn't hear the bell. David, are you the referee or the croupier?'

It was one of those nights, full of action, and despite Alec, the tips were pretty good. There were no spare seats, people were standing, calling bets as punters, trying to share banks with seated players. It was all go and I had to be on my toes.

Cathy showed up around one o'clock, looking more

vulnerable than usual, as if she'd been crying. After another hour, at the end of the shoe, one of the players suggested a ten minute break – we had been playing for four hours. The players got up and went out of the smoke-filled room, Tommy and Malky now seeming to be the best of pals. Gina, the chemmy room waitress, brought us coffee and Cathy told me she'd had a row with her brother. I didn't even know she had a brother. There wasn't much time to talk as play had to restart. The game finished two hours later and it didn't take long to wrap everything up.

On the way home she started crying and told me she also had a kid, Lisa, a girl of seven who was living with her mother and brother. It seemed her brother was in big trouble with the police. We were nearly back at my flat in Whitley Bay by then and it was just getting light. I turned onto the coast road, past the Spanish City funfair and the Rex Hotel, and parked near the ruined Priory overlooking the sea. The forbidding, cold, steel grey North Sea.

Cathy lit a cigarette and sat there staring. I asked her to tell me the whole story, suggested maybe I could help. She told me her dad had died when she was ten and that she and her older brother, Jimmy, were brought up by their mother in Gateshead. Seven years ago, when she was nineteen, she had the kid, Lisa. The father was living abroad and never got in touch. Her best friend, Vicky, had gone on a training course in London to be a croupier and was making good money so

Cathy decided to do the same and give it a go for a year. She left Lisa with her mother and Jimmy said he would help. But Jimmy had got involved in handling stolen goods. He was due in court the following month and very likely would get a prison sentence. It would screw up all Cathy's plans.

And that's exactly what happened. Jimmy got six months and was fined three thousand pounds which had to be paid within a year, otherwise he would do another two years in prison. Cathy moved back home to Gateshead from where she drove me mad to get her a job in the casino but we had too many croupiers as it was. Then Gina left to have a baby. You could earn a lot of money working the chemmy room.

I got Cathy the job.

13

Maple Court, 10:05 a.m.

I'm restless. There are still nearly two hours before the taxi is due and my mind is racing to and fro. What exactly happened? What is going to happen? When I look back at the events and that period when my life changed so dramatically, it's as if time has been stretched. Six months then seems like years now.

I look round the room at the furnishings I took such care in choosing. They belong to someone else now. What's left of my possessions fit into a small cardboard box and a leather suitcase.

14

Cathy's brother Jimmy came out of prison after serving three months. It had scared the life out of him. He looked terrible. With no chance of paying the fine of three thousand pounds he was desperate at the thought of going back inside.

Jimmy was friendly enough, quite good-looking, just a bit weak and bitter. It showed. There was something about him that was slightly worn, as if he was wearing someone else's clothes. His surname was Fish and a cruel woodwork teacher had once called him *Slippery Fish*. It had stuck all through secondary school, apparently, and fifteen years later, he was still known as Slippery. He asked me for a loan and I gave him twenty pounds which I didn't expect back.

Jimmy and I were polar opposites. He was desperate, frightened, out of work, had no confidence, no self-esteem and was now a convicted criminal. I felt sorry for him. I'd always thought it would only take a few wrong moves to finish up in trouble and that there was a side to me that courted risk too much for my own good.

Maybe I should have given more thought to Jimmy's problems but I was getting on with my life, working and playing hard. Cathy was a part of it. She was back living with her mother and Lisa but sometimes she stayed at my place. The whole time I was with her I never met Lisa or her mother or went into their home. We didn't discuss much, not how we felt about each other or what we did when we weren't with each other. I knew I wasn't in love with her but I found her sexually impossible to resist. She would do anything anywhere. Sex seemed to be her great release.

Cathy was disparaging of the people who were giving her a lot of money for serving them coffee and sandwiches. I think she resented successful people and couldn't handle being a waitress. Like her brother she was bitter, angry about something. I found out later that they'd all – including their mother – had a bad time with the father. I think he was violent and had pushed them around. Cathy hated him, was glad he was dead and felt sorry for her mother. She, herself, was a loner. Other than Vicky she had few, if any, friends. Jimmy was probably the only person she could turn to. I got the impression that she both looked up to him and at the same time was completely protective of him.

It's odd to spend time with somebody, have sex with

them regularly and not really like them. But that's the way it was with Cathy and me. She was critical of everything and always felt hard done by. It showed in the downward turn of her mouth – unfortunate because it detracted from her beautiful face. The one thing she seemed to like, besides sex, was music. She was obsessed with Frank Sinatra and played his records incessantly. I never saw her read a book, only fashion magazines. She went to the hairdresser every week and was forever filing her nails. She was quite a heavy smoker and immediately after sex lit a cigarette, which I hated.

◆

A couple of months after Jimmy came out of prison I had a very bad night. I ran into a seven timer.

I'd been gambling at the Victoria from early evening and was doing well. A full chemmy table was on the go, one roulette table was open with half a dozen punters, a few spectators were hanging around and it had that end of the night, time to go home, feeling.

At five in the morning, a thousand pounds in front, due to catch a noon flight, the smart move was to cash in, pick up my bags at the Hilton, and cab it to the airport. Sure – until from nowhere I was in a *suivi* nightmare. In chemmy, when a punter (in this case me) bets against the bank by calling *banco* – the whole amount that's in the bank – and loses, they then have the right to call *banco suivi*. This is a follow-on bet against the bank, that is, providing the bank doesn't get passed on and the punter once again calls the whole amount that's in the bank.

The bank was with a very attractive older woman, wearing a low-cut, purple evening dress. She had a strong, almost masculine face. She put forty pounds in the bank and I called, '*Banco*.' She smiled at me as she dealt the cards from the shoe. I smiled back and looked at my two cards – a four of clubs and a three of diamonds – a total of seven. Nice. 'No card,' I said. She turned over her cards, the jack of spades and the eight of hearts.

'*Huit a la banque*,' the croupier announced. The woman had won.

She let the eighty pounds ride and I called, '*Banco suivi*.' She – the bank – won again.

So it continued. She kept letting it ride. I kept calling *banco suivi* and losing. I was playing *her*, not the run of the cards. After five consecutive wins by the bank, I had lost one thousand two hundred and forty pounds – my earlier winnings and two hundred and forty of my own money. There was now twelve hundred and eighty pounds in the bank and I only had another couple of hundred pounds cash left. If I wanted to call the whole amount I would need more money.

I informed the croupier that I would like to cash a cheque. He signalled to the floor supervisor who approached the table. The woman in purple looked almost apologetic. She turned to the croupier and said, 'The gentleman can call the bet if he would like to do so.' Meanwhile I was playing Mr Cool, the nonchalant gambler, trying hard not to show my irritation. I had no right to still be sitting there. Less than five minutes ago I was winning a grand and now I was trapped, chasing losses.

I smiled at her and said, 'Thank you.' She smiled back. No doubt she was thinking better to let a loser carry on than let anybody else try their luck.

The supervisor, now standing by my side, said to the croupier, 'The house will cover the gentleman's bet.' Turning to me, he quietly said, 'That's fine David we can sort this out later.' He added even more quietly, 'We can cover this bet and one more *suivi* should that be necessary.' He went over to the croupier whispered something to him and walked away. I was such an ego merchant, I felt good about being given the chance of losing even more money.

A handful of punters from the roulette table were now watching. As soon as there's a smell of action in a casino, the watchers appear. I was feeling uncomfortable, slightly sweaty – guaranteed to lose. And I did. In three minutes I lost that hand – twelve hundred and eighty pounds. I called *suivi* again and lost the next one – two thousand five hundred and sixty pounds. The woman never stopped smiling sympathetically and I never stopped playing to the gallery.

I stood up, trying not to appear concerned, went over to the cash desk and wrote out a cheque for three thousand eight hundred and forty pounds. Chasing forty pounds, I'd lost my earlier winnings and over four grand of my own money. I could have bought a brand new Aston Martin DB5 for that.

My float and savings were gone and with zero in the pot I was not pleased with myself on the flight back. I was mentally checking if I had enough money to play poker at the weekend, when the stewardess asked, 'Would you like a drink sir?' She was really nice and before we landed she gave me her telephone number. I knew everything was fine. As long as you can get back in the game you've got a chance. And it wouldn't take that long for me to get back in.

15

Maple Court, 10:09 a.m.

I'm gazing out the window of the flat, looking not at what is in front of me but back there in the past somewhere. I'm impatient to leave, to escape. I've always been trying to escape.

I'm moving on with no idea of what I'm going to do next. I only know what I'm giving up. Maybe I never really thought I was entitled to what I'd acquired. Why does good fortune have to be an undeserved gift?

My expensive trappings I'd disposed of without any pain. Whatever you do, you can't escape the past, though. I turn back to the room and look around. There is only the pack of cards and Helen's book left on the table.

◆

Helen, the woman who had been in charge of the library trolley, was the only person I had kept in touch with from Baguley Sanatorium. We would write to each other every couple of months and occasionally meet for coffee. She continued to influence my reading. Unlike my mum and Denise, she wasn't critical of my new life. It seemed to amuse her and she would get me to describe everything I was doing in detail. And I mean everything, from gambling to my sexual exploits.

There was always a growing air of sadness about Helen. She was in a loveless marriage. She'd met her husband, Steve, at university. They married when she was twenty, had no kids and she was bored. Steve was making pots of money as a senior brand manager for Procter and Gamble. He didn't want her to work full-time and expected her to entertain the numerous business contacts he regularly brought home.

One time, Helen and I arranged to meet in the Kardomah Café, the fashionable place to go. It was where my pals and I often went, spending hours chatting and messing about. One of the lads, who sold bolts of cloth from his car boot, had business cards printed with the Kardomah as his office address.

I was there early and saw her arrive. She was wearing a tightly-belted, floral summer dress, open at the neck. She looked lovely. We hugged and ordered coffee. We'd only been there a short time when she unexpectedly asked if I would like to come to her house for dinner that night. I knew her husband was frequently away, travelling, so I said, 'Yes, I'd love to.' We didn't stay much longer. As soon as we got in the car she put her hand on my thigh.

'Why don't you stay the night,' she suggested.

'That sounds great,' I replied.

She lived in Poynton, southeast of Manchester, in a large, newly-built, neo-Georgian detached house, suffocatingly furnished in reproduction antiques. One room was effectively a library with wall-to-wall bookshelves, two big armchairs and a writing desk. There was a small parcel on the desk. 'That's for you,' Helen said, handing it to me. I opened it. It was a book, *The Gambler* by Dostoevsky.

'Thank you. This is a surprise.' I didn't just mean the gift.

'Read and take heed,' she said laughing. 'He wrote it to pay off his gambling debts.'

I loved the 19th century image on the front cover, a painting by Robert Shore, somebody I hadn't heard of. Bathed in a magenta hue, a desperate-looking young man is standing in front of a double-sided roulette table, staring out. He's wearing a black tailcoat with a purple-grey waistcoat, white silk cravat and frilled cuffs. Behind him there are spectators standing, players seated, all staring at him. He looks like he's just blown all his money. He was the spitting image of Charlie Wise, a Geordie car dealer, who was always losing and couldn't accept he played badly. His catchphrase was, 'I've been a fool to myself.'

I didn't mind that Helen had planned everything that night. She was in control and I liked it. She was a great cook, the food was delicate, the wine superb. She told me about a book she was reading, *The Group* by Mary McCarthy, which she thought I would enjoy. 'If nothing else, it will contribute to your understanding of women. And possibly men,' she added with a smile. She was relaxed and enjoying herself.

After dinner she insisted I go into the lounge while she cleared up and made coffee.

Apart from the large, cream-coloured brocade sofa and matching armchair, there was a formality about the room that gave it the feel of a Harley Street dentist's waiting room. I opened *The Gambler*. I hadn't read any Dostoevsky before. I was immediately drawn into a tragic story of tortured love and gambling addiction. My kind of book.

When Helen came in, we drank coffee and brandy without rushing, looking forward to what was to follow. She was sitting close to me on the sofa. She put her hand on my thigh again, 'Shall we go to bed now?' she asked, smiling. I nodded, yes.

She took my hand and led me upstairs to the bedroom. The bed was covered in a mountain of scatter cushions which Helen carefully placed on the two bedroom chairs by the dressing table. The curtains were already drawn and one of the bedside lights was on.

'You don't have to use contraceptives, I'm on the pill,'

she said matter-of-factly, 'but I would like to switch the light off.'

'That's okay Helen,' I said softly and turned the lamp off.

She gently took charge of our lovemaking. It was liberating. While Cathy was aggressively dominating, Helen was gently in control. She was completely at ease in bed. It was as if everything she knew or had read about sex she wanted to experience that night.

It was the most erotic night I'd ever had with anyone.

I'd always found lots of women beautiful for different reasons: the way they moved, spoke, laughed, tossed their hair, not just because of their looks or bodies. I'd never been with a woman so much older than me. It made me realise how irrelevant age can be when there's sexual attraction.

In the morning, after breakfast, she said to me, 'I loved you last night, David.'

It was a statement about a night we spent together, no more. I loved her for saying it and told her so.

In the hallway, as we were about to say goodbye, she said, 'I don't know when I'll see you again. My husband has been transferred to Manila and, of course, I have to go with him.'

'I'll miss you,' I said. It was all I could say. We stood looking at each other. Then hugged without saying anything more. I got in the car and drove back into Manchester.

I thought of going to see Denise but felt guilty.

Instead, I went to see Wolfie.

When I got to his place there were five lit *yahrtzeit* candles on the table. We sat down, he opened a bottle of schnapps, took off his glasses, half-closed his eyes and peered into the past. I never asked him about his past. When he was ready he would talk. It was always as if he was talking about somebody else. I listened without speaking.

He carried on talking and we carried on drinking until it was dark and then we went to the French Room at the Midland Hotel and had the best wine and food.

... After they had been on the train for five days the doors to the cattle car were unlocked. Of the hundred or more people jammed into the car, less than twenty were still alive, including him and his eldest brother. In all the pandemonium he thought he saw his brother say something to one of the poor creatures in striped pyjamas pushing them down the ramp. Then his brother turned to him and in Yiddish said, "Tell these bastards you're eighteen and a tailor." They were the last words he heard his brother say.

16

Cathy couldn't stop talking about what was going to happen to Jimmy if he couldn't pay the fine. I knew that she was expecting me to help. Three thousand pounds was a lot and it wasn't something I spent any time thinking about; especially now that I'd done my money.

When she didn't show up one Saturday night, I knew something was wrong but there was no way I could contact her. I'd have to go round to her mother's the next day or wait for her to call the club. It was about half nine when she rang. I took the call on the front desk. She was crying. Something had happened to Jimmy and he was in the General Hospital. He was going to be okay but it was serious. He'd tried to commit suicide.

I couldn't leave until the chemmy was over. I got to the hospital just after 3:30 a.m. and met Cathy at reception. As soon as she saw me she burst into tears. 'We've got to help him.

He'll do it again. I know he will,' she sobbed.

'How is he now?' I asked.

'They've moved him on to the wards, thank God.'

I hate hospitals. The last time I was in one was the night Dad died. Before that it had been Baguley. I wasn't scared of them. I just couldn't bear to be in them. Cathy sensed my unease and quickly filled me in. Jimmy had taken well over a hundred aspirins, had panicked and got her to call an ambulance. This had all happened as she was about to go to work. Luckily she hadn't left.

'Maybe it was an accident,' I said, lamely.

'Nobody goes out and buys three bottles of aspirin then swallows the lot accidentally,' Cathy retorted.

She was pretty upset and I didn't reply. I put my arms round her and was quiet. She looked like a kid.

'He's asleep now and the nurse said it would be better if I came back in the morning,' she said. 'Why don't we go back to yours?'

She fell asleep as soon as I started driving.

Jimmy looked strange when we saw him later that morning. His face was puffy, with red blotches and he was sweating. He didn't want to talk. The doctor appeared and explained that Jimmy was going to be fine but they were keeping him in for a few days to keep an eye on him. I left Cathy with Jimmy and went to the cafeteria. Maybe he would talk if I wasn't there.

I saw the doctor in the lift and asked him what was going on. He was surprisingly forthcoming. He referred to it as a failed suicide attempt. He said it was more than likely that Jimmy had no actual intention of killing himself and it was probably a cry for help. Given Jimmy's situation I couldn't help thinking he was right.

The cafeteria was grim but at least it wasn't green. Supposedly hospital walls and uniforms are green because blood doesn't show up so easily on green and it's for harmony and all that. But does it have to be puke green? Cathy came in after a while and said we should go. The nurse thought it was better to let Jimmy sleep for the rest of the day and we could come back tomorrow. I told Cathy what the doctor had said. She laughed and told me it didn't take a genius to work that out and what were *we* – meaning me – going to do about stopping him from trying it again. In other words, 'Pay his fine, David, and prevent him from going back to prison.'

'Why don't we go to The George, have something to eat and talk about it?' I suggested. Cathy liked it there. It was out west, near Hexham, a quiet country pub with great food.

'That would be nice,' she said, linking my arm as we walked to my white Mercedes 220SE Coupé. It had black leather bucket seats in the front, as big as armchairs. It drove like a dream at over a hundred miles an hour and we headed out of town on roads notoriously fast and dangerous.

This was Hadrian's Wall territory, frontier of the

Roman Empire, where they had kept the warring Picts at bay more or less successfully for three hundred years: beautiful, rugged moorland with the North Pennines to the south and Northumberland National Park to the north. We hardly spoke, drinking in the countryside, enjoying the power of the car. It was too late for lunch, too early for dinner, so we had afternoon tea, the usual: sandwiches, scones, cakes.

We stayed a couple of hours then drove back. I told Cathy I wanted to help Jimmy but had lost all my money. I could find something but nowhere near enough to save Jimmy from prison. I could tell she was pissed off. She didn't say much only that she would think of a solution. When we got to Newcastle she said she wanted to go back to her mother's – via the golf course car park. Meaning she wanted to have sex. For some time she'd seemed to prefer sex in the car more than anywhere. Fine by me.

It was dark by the time we got to the empty car park. I parked at the far end, away from the entrance and switched off the lights. She told me to lower my seat back. Then she slowly and deliberately took off all her clothes.

Afterwards she said, 'Was that good?'

I told her, 'It was fantastic,' because it was.

At which she looked at and me and said, 'I'm not fucking you again until we agree on a way to help Jimmy.' We drove to her mother's in silence. As she got out the car she turned to me and said, 'I mean it.'

Jimmy came out of hospital three days later. Cathy came into work on the Friday and said he was much better. We saw each other at work the following week. It was a bit odd but so what, it was her choice to withhold sex and an unreasonable one at that. I couldn't help but feel that this was something she had been thinking about for some time. She was all too aware of how much I was drawn to her sexually. Then, on Saturday, after the chemmy game, she asked me if I would give her a lift home. When I stopped the car, she started kissing me, but stopped from going any further. 'I want you to come to London with me,' she whispered.

'When? Why?' I asked.

'As soon as we can, next week. I want you to meet a friend of Vicky's.'

'Who?'

'You'll find out when we get there. It's a surprise.'

'Okay.' I agreed. Why not? Maybe she'd changed her mind about 'fucking'. Anyway, it was likely to be a quiet week, we had nobody big on and Harry and Joseph would be fine about me taking a break.

Little did I realise what Cathy's surprise would be.

17

Maple Court, 10:20 a.m.

I hear the sea.

I remember my cigar case. It's still in my jacket hanging in the wardrobe. There's one cigar still in the case.

I suppose I was quite young to have become a cigar smoker but it's easy to acquire expensive habits when you have money.

I light up. What a taste. The aroma – tranquil, a nutty combination of chocolate and coffee. So good. I've still got a bottle of Hine brandy that the brewery rep gave me. Something a bit special, with a hand-written label. I get it from the bookcase bar and pour a generous shot. Looking at myself in the hall mirror, savouring the moment, wryly saluting the past, beckoning the future, I say out loud, 'Cheers. Best of luck, David.'

I want to put a record on but don't want to take anything out of the cardboard box. I sit down on the sofa and listen to the sound of the sea, the North Sea, a soothing backing for the circling, screeching gulls. They demand answers. 'Why? Why? Why? Who are you? What are you doing? Where are you going? Why? Why? Why?'

Why did I go to London with Cathy?

18

'The Carnival is Over' by the Seekers had been at number-one for three weeks. There was a huge Christmas tree in the front lobby of the May Fair.

It was snowing when we left Newcastle but mild and clear in London. Cathy wanted to go out immediately, to meet Vicky and her mysterious friend. We took a taxi, 'Isow's,' Cathy told the driver and off we went.

Jack Isow's famous restaurant in Soho. I'd been before but didn't say anything to Cathy. The food was all right, nothing special. Lots of showbiz people ate there. I remembered the big red chairs on which were embossed the names of movie stars who had been there.

When Cathy told the waiter we were meeting Vicky Alan, he looked at the reservations, nodded and led us to a table at the back. Vicky was there on her own. She jumped up and kissed Cathy, then me.

'You must be David,' she said. 'I'm Vicky. George isn't here yet, but he's on his way. Sit down, I've just got here. Let's have a drink.'

Vicky was small, dark, attractive and spoke very fast. Her real name was Alanis and she came from Cyprus.

'Slow down, Vicky, you'll make David nervous,' Cathy said, laughing.

We sat down. My chair had Kirk Douglas on the back. Cathy looked at hers and said, 'Ooh, I'm Bette Davis.'

Vicky added, 'Well, I'm Diana Dors.'

We all started laughing.

I ordered a Coke and they had Babychams. They were giggling and making faces, talking non-stop about The Vic and who was still working there, who was going out with whom. I wasn't listening. I was enjoying relaxing, looking round, seeing who was in the restaurant. Then out the corner of my eye I saw this figure and had a funny feeling. He was tall, lean, olive-skinned with soft brown eyes, wearing a well-cut light grey, double-breasted suit. He was coming over to our table, smiling. Vicky saw him too and stood up, saying, 'George, you're here.'

He looked just like my Dad.

He bent down, took Vicky's hand and kissed it. '*Yiasou*, Vicky, sweetheart, how wonderful to see you'. He looked at Cathy and me and said, 'And who are these two young film stars?' He was so obviously insincere yet I liked him immediately. He was a market worker, a pitch puller.

'This is Cathy, I'm David, and you're a good act,' I said.

'It takes one to know one.' He gave a huge grin and sat down next to me. 'Let's eat. It's my treat. We have *meze*. Too early in the day to have a big meal. Manny!' He called out the waiter's name. Manny shuffled over and George reeled off a bunch of different starters. As the waiter was about to go, George touched his arm and in a half-whisper said, 'And bring some champagne, you know what I like.'

We ate, drank and smoked cigars. He told us his real name was Giorgios. I never found out his surname. He was a Greek Cypriot who had come to England in 1930 when he was fifteen. Like most of the young men from his homeland, he settled in North London, joining a small community that had swelled after Cyprus became a Crown Colony in 1925. George loved Cyprus and spoke passionately about the land and the people, pointing out, 'You not the boss now, we have our country back.' It was true. Five years earlier, in 1960, Cyprus had gained its independence and ceased to be under British rule. At first he had worked in his uncle's cafe in Camden. When his uncle died he became apprenticed to a local shoemaker. He hated the work, 'Not for me,' he said emphatically. 'I find a better way to earn a living than killing myself, day after day, year after year, breathing dust and glue. I become a professional gambler, hmm, fifteen years ago.' He shook his head knowingly and said, 'Big money. Big, big money.'

In what seemed no time, we'd been there three hours. George said he had to leave but wanted to meet Cathy and me later. Before I had time to say anything she agreed and we were shaking hands, arranging to meet him at the May Fair Hotel that evening. He shook hands in a two-handed way, conveying more warmth than expected. He had the largest hands I'd ever seen.

◆

Outside, in the street there was just Cathy and me. Vicky was on an early shift at the Victoria.

'What d'you fancy doing?' I asked Cathy.

'Going back to the May Fair and fucking,' she whispered in my ear.

I didn't argue.

Later, smugly, I said, 'So much for no sex until we had a plan for helping Jimmy.'

She laughed and said, 'I have. You'll see.'

That evening at eight o'clock reception rang to say, 'A Mr George is here to see you.' I checked with Cathy if maybe we should go down.

'No, tell them to send him up,' she exclaimed.

When Cathy let him in, he was carrying a brown paper bag. We shook hands, and with a smile, he handed me the bag.

'A gift from the home of the gods,' he whispered.

I thanked him, put the bag on the table and took out the contents. A very odd-looking inch thick candle which in fact was a chewy sweet made from grape juice and with a nutty almond centre, and a bottle of colourless spirit with the name Zivania on the label.

George produced a penknife and began to chop the candle into slices, saying, 'This is soutzoukos, comes from the mountains near my village and this, zivania.' Picking up the bottle he opened it, offering it to me. 'Smell.' I couldn't place the faint aroma. He laughed. 'Raisins, raisins. And now a little of each.'

We found three glasses and he poured a shot in each glass. It was surprisingly cold and harsh. The soutzoukos helped greatly.

George and I were sitting at an occasional table. Cathy was propped up on the bed. It was as if everything was in limbo. George told us he came from Latchi on the north-west end of the island of Cyprus. With tears in his eyes he spoke about growing up in a small fishing village, its beautiful quiet beaches and warm sparkling sea. He recounted the tale of Aphrodite meeting Adonis at the baths as if he had been there. He was a sentimental charmer, a storyteller, a professional gambler who read Homer and Ovid.

Putting his hand inside his jacket he produced a pack of Waddingtons Number 1 playing cards and handed them to me. They were unopened, the cellophane was intact and the seal unbroken. 'Do you like card tricks, David?' he asked.

'Sometimes,' I said.

'Open the pack.'

I did as he said. Cathy was now sitting on the edge of the bed, watching very closely what was going on.

'Shuffle, deal the cards slowly face down and turn them over when I say.'

I gave them a good shuffle and started to deal the cards onto the table carefully.

'Turn it over,' George instructed. 'Is an eight or nine. Turn it over, is an eight or nine. Turn it over is an eight or nine.' He called out all the eights and nines in the pack.

Cathy, like a child, kept shouting, 'How d'you do that, how d'you do that?' At one point she snatched an eight card from the table and kept turning it over, scrutinising its back and front, shaking her head before throwing it back on the table in disgust.

'I show you one more thing, then I tell you.' George picked up the cards which seemed to shrink in his huge hands. Pulling out the four aces, he put them on the top of the pack. He shuffled fast, expertly and apparently very thoroughly, then gave the pack to me. 'Turn them over.'

Of course the four aces were still on the top. 'Okay,' I said, 'you're doing a false shuffle and the cards are marked.'

'Correct. But the question is, how? Where?' He picked

up the cards and said, 'Show me.' Then handed them to me.

'They were a new pack, weren't they?' Cathy asked impatiently.

They were just a regular pack of blue-backed Waddingtons with the familiar symmetrical design on the back. I looked and looked, held them near to the bedside lamp, but still I couldn't see anything unusual.

'Look, I show you,' George said.

Cathy and I gathered round him, like kids round Santa. He handed both of us cards he'd marked. Only after he physically pointed to it could we see the mark where he'd shaded a minuscule part of the scroll border, in the centre of the two long sides of the card. Once he showed us what he'd done, it was as if he'd put flashing lights on the eights and nines. He pointed to his handiwork and proudly said, 'Look is good, very good, is very light work, impossible to tell unless you know.' His eyes narrowing, he whispered seriously, 'Two things – this and the pull through shuffle. We make a fortune quick.'

'But they were brand new packs,' Cathy insisted.

'It take me ten minutes to open and reseal. Easy. Not so easy marking six packs ... hours to do it properly, just the right touch of shading.'

'Levels of darkness,' I said to myself, out loud.

'What does that mean?' George asked.

'Shading is just different levels of darkness,' I muttered.

Something Denise had said when she was doing one of her sketches.

Now I knew where he was heading. Chemmy. The only card game I was aware of that used six packs of cards and where eights and nines ruled. Knowing when the eights or nines were coming out would be most advantageous and the overall chance of becoming a winner would increase significantly.

I anticipated his pitch but what I didn't expect was the sheer chutzpah of the proposal he was about to make. Alarmingly, even though I was sure he was a crook, I continued to be drawn to him, not wanting his performance to end.

On top of substituting genuine decks for marked decks, George presented the outrageous idea of planting, in one of the six packs, a sequence of cards set in a prearranged order – a *slug* – enabling a cheat to bet with certainty on the outcome of a known combination of cards. In chemmy, slugs invariably include a run of winning hands for the bank. Knowing the exact number of times a bank will win, the card sharp can back the bank where possible. Bet against the bank when the winning sequence comes to an end, and if the bank should land with him when the slug appears, maximise his potential winnings.

Planting the slug, was where George's false shuffle came into play. The four aces had remained on top, undisturbed, in his little trick, because he'd used a combined riffle and pull-through shuffle. He did that by cutting the deck approximately in half, placing the halves flat on the table with their rear corners touching, then lifting the back edges with his thumbs while pushing the two halves together. By doing that, the cards were riffled – interleaved. And by using little or no pressure the interleaved halves were pushed together at an angle, allowing the dealer – George, here – to take hold of one half, pull it through and place it on top of the other half without disturbing any of the cards. The final moment of the pull-through was done in such a way that it was as if the cards had been squared up and cut. However, the cards remained in exactly the same order as they were before the shuffle and cut.

It's a dazzling crooked shuffle requiring considerable practice.

Planting a pre-arranged slug deck alongside the other decks in the shoe is extremely tricky. It requires the complicity of the croupier running the game. The croupier has to retain control over the rigged pack, open it, do a pull-through shuffle, then ensure it goes in undisturbed with the other five decks as they are put in the shoe.

When sealed decks are displayed on the table in advance of the game starting, switching the genuine packs for the crooked ones is easy. It becomes a question of when, not how. The cards being marked is a minor risk. It's difficult to prove who has switched the genuine packs or who has marked them. For a croupier to control and plant a pre-arranged slug pack requires risk-taking on a totally different scale. It is so difficult to pull off that it is rarely undertaken.

Chemmy was wide open to cheating, especially in small casinos. It's a game that often takes place in a private room, in an informal atmosphere, with players who know each other. Big gamblers are frequently given licence to lark about, are allowed to handle the cards, especially at the very beginning of play. It gives them a false sense of security, a feeling that they are in control. A cunning croupier is able to exploit this, handing out packs to be shuffled by the players as he thinks fit, retaining control of the slug pack, diverting attention away from what he is doing.

George knew all this and no doubt I wasn't the first croupier he'd reeled in. His pitch made it all seem so easy and almost acceptable. 'What difference?' He shrugged. 'All we are doing is changing the odds in our favour and even then we could still lose. There's no need to decide now. I'll come to Newcastle and then we can talk some more.'

Like all good conmen, he knew when not to push it. He was charming, persuasive, a ruthless exploiter of any human weakness. He poured another drink, saying, '*Yamas*. Don't worry, David. Is all fine, easier than you think. Believe me.'

It was dark outside, and the room lit by the bedside table lamps and two floor lamps, gave a warm comforting glow to our Faustian pact. Picking up the cards again George said, 'Let me show you how to do a pull-through shuffle. Whatever happens, is a fun trick.'

I was all too willing a pupil, a fast learner, and after half an hour we both knew that within a short time I would be very good. How quickly I was primed to trade in my morals and the trust of friends, in a scam to make money.

Cathy was a bystander, her job as the go-between done. She would come to play an important part in the execution of the eventual scam, but that was later. I don't remember her saying anything else until George had gone. Then, she couldn't wait to go on about it. 'This could be just what we're looking for. You could get your savings back. We could help Jimmy.'

'I don't know. I don't like it,' I said.

'You don't like it. Who cares. What about saving Jimmy's life?' she said angrily. 'We've got to help him. I told him we would.'

'You shouldn't have promised something you can't do.'

'What would you do, wait for him to try and kill himself again?' she shouted.

I was hearing but not listening. Why was all this shit about her brother being laid on me? He was a crook and now she wanted me to get involved in a scam to help him. 'He's conning you,' I said. 'If he wanted to kill himself, he'd have done it.'

'You're an arsehole.' Pointing her index finger in my face, she repeatedly screamed, 'Arsehole, arsehole, arsehole!'

I grabbed hold of her finger, told her she was the arsehole and pushed her onto the bed. Now she was laughing. In between us both shouting 'arsehole' and laughing, we were pulling each other's clothes off. We ordered room service, finished off George's zivania and continued enjoying each other.

We stayed in bed until noon, had breakfast in the room, went shopping on the King's Road. That was the now-familiar catwalk of crazies and stunning, exotic women and men, enjoying the competition and the attention. To walk just over a mile from the Royal Court Theatre on Sloane Square (showing a play called *Saved* which Denise had told me was causing a right to do) to the World's End pub, we had to push our way along pavements crowded with people spilling on to the road. We passed girls in incredibly short mini-skirts, blokes in every colour of velvet imaginable, a Jesus look-alike wearing an avocado green suit with a tame white rat on his shoulder, two film crews, a wedding party outside Chelsea Old Town Hall, and hordes of young people diving in and out of innumerable boutiques, bistros and cafes from which blared the competing sounds of the Kinks, the Rolling Stones, the Who, and Uncle Tom Cobley and all. We trailed the endless boutiques for a couple of hours buying an array of gear, which would no doubt raise eyebrows back up North. After one of my shopping expeditions I went home with a pink shirt and a black and white polka dot tie which earned me plenty of comments.

Cathy wanted to see *The Cincinnati Kid*. Luckily I'd seen it because I wasn't in the mood to watch a film about gambling, especially one with such a far-fetched ending. Instead, we went to see *Repulsion*, a film Denise had told me about, very strange, dark. I liked it, but Cathy hated it and wanted to leave halfway. For once I won the argument and we stayed. Afterwards, we went for salt beef, chips and pickled cucumbers at The Nosh Bar in Soho, then cabbed it back to the hotel. We were soon sipping Mai Tai cocktails and listening to the sound of ukuleles and slack-key guitars in the Beachcomber, the May Fair's Polynesian restaurant bar. Beyond the over-the-top décor – totem poles, fishing nets, sculptured ship figureheads, waterfalls and tropical thunderstorms – was a restaurant serving high-end cuisine where only the wealthy dined.

Everything was cool. It was the swinging sixties in London and I was enjoying the fruits of cultural change. Gambling, money, sex, rubbing shoulders with pop stars. But apart from music and mini skirts, I wasn't sure how much of this was happening anywhere else. Long hair, the pill and lava lamps were all fine but for most people it was grim out there.

We steered clear of talking about George and had a good night. It was as if the unspoken words and the intrigue were pushing us together, turning us on.

... *The boy thought about his aunt who was blind. Whenever he used to go and see her she would get him to stand in front of her. Touching and feeling his face she would always repeat the same words of endearment, 'Lovely boy, handsome boy, shayne punim.' Then she would take money out of her pocket and push it into his hand.*

He hadn't seen her since the round up and had no idea where she was.

19

Maple Court, 10:35 a.m.

I open the pack of cards and start dealing out five hands of five-card stud. I would do this for hours at a time, playing all the hands, noting the chances of making winning hands and the futility of playing with poor cards.

I was about eight when I first heard "The Deck of Cards" by Tex Ritter. I wasn't sure about it even then but I did like his rendition of "High Noon" and we would all try to imitate his rich baritone voice.

I keep dealing and thinking. Thinking and dealing ...

20

The week after Cathy and I went to London, George rang to say he was coming to the Copacabana on the Saturday. He wanted to recce the club and the chemmy game. Obviously, he warned, we would not let on we knew each other. I told him I hadn't decided anything yet. I didn't mention I'd been practising the pull-through shuffle, kidding myself it was just another party trick.

I conveniently pushed George to the back of my mind and was almost surprised to see him walk into the chemmy room with Harry. Ever the conman, he'd literally spun a yarn about being in textiles and said he was on his way up to Scotland on a buying trip. He told Harry that he loved to gamble and had heard good things about the club. He sat in on the game, genial, betting flamboyantly, losing good-humouredly, winning graciously and tipping generously. A sophisticated gambler. He left about midnight, quietly telling Cathy where he was staying and suggesting we meet the following afternoon.

We did meet. I agreed to go along with the scam.

Why do some of the most important events of your life happen as if by accident, so casually that you can hardly remember when or how? Maybe it's because in those events we want to block out, we want to take on the role of the innocent bystander, not the perpetrator or the willing accomplice. I'd felt guilty ever since I told Cathy that Jimmy's attempted suicide was a con. How did I know what Jimmy was going through? Making amends by helping Jimmy now provided the perfect excuse for my own potential misdeeds. It wouldn't take long to forget what the real reasons were for doing what I did. I was in denial about it being fraudulent, or that the scam could be viewed as harmful. I was helping to save Jimmy's life. I was averting a violent act.

Violence can take many forms. The most violent encounter I experienced in my time in nightclubs was when I happened to be at the front desk and Lindsay, a notorious local hoodlum banned from the club, tried to get in. The frightened doorman, passing the buck, turned to me and said, 'What do you think, David?' Before I could say anything Lindsay walked up to me, putting his Cro Magnon head in butting distance from my face.

'Yeah, what do you think, David?' he snarled.

'It's not up to me,' I choked.

'Let's go outside and sort this out,' grunted Lindsay – meaning step into the ally while I kick your head in.

'I'm not doing that,' I said.

He looked at me, nodded, then took hold of the middle button of my expensive mohair dinner suit, twisted it and pulled it off, leaving a jagged hole in my jacket. *That's my head*, I thought.

'I'll see you,' he threatened. And walked out the door.

Against encounters like that it was easy for me to rationalise that what I was doing was a non-violent caper, not really harming anybody, indeed I was doing the opposite, helping a fellow human being. And anyway, all George and I were really doing was increasing the odds in our favour, a bit like the house introducing a double zero from a single zero on a roulette wheel, almost doubling its edge from 2.7% to 5.26%.

That's the psychological game. Detach yourself from the guilt by morally justifying the scam and if possible compare it to the duplicity of others, especially the establishment, whoever they might be.

I can't say I thought about what I was doing, how much I would make, whether or not I would get caught, or what would happen to me if I did. It wasn't a rational decision. I could have got my losses back soon enough. I wasn't responsible for Jimmy. I didn't have to do it.

But I did do it.

And I didn't need to do it.

Why does anybody step over the honesty line? On my first Saturday market job I was selling shoes. My boss told me, 'If a customer says the shoes are too tight, go round the back of the stall and if we haven't got a bigger size, bring back the same pair and tell them it's the next size up.' It worked nine times out of ten. Was that simply a laugh or the slippery slope? If I was undercharged in a restaurant, that was their problem, whereas Denise, for example, would tell the waiter. If your accountant massages your expenses is that a crime or fair game?

Presumably George had learned to cheat from somebody, like I was learning to cheat from him. Who knows why anybody cheats? Some people never get the opportunity; don't have a reason to; don't want to. George, the master manipulator, had a simple three-pronged strategy: clock the opportunity, teach the modus operandi, and throw in some moral rationalisation.

Conmen often dive into obscurity, they don't all live in swish places. Maybe they need to hide away, keep out the light. George rented a seedy flat in Jesmond and on the nights we knew he would be in town, we called in to his place to pick up the marked decks. Cathy would put them in her handbag and switch them before the game. At first it was just a case of switching packs, relying on the marked cards to ensure we won. Then as we got greedier we became more ambitious, using the slug to guarantee a run of winning hands.

George used a formula for putting the slug in a particular

order, which meant he always knew exactly when the winning sequence was about to come out. As long as I didn't disturb the slug deck all was okay. Occasionally I did disturb the sequence and it would go wrong. No matter, we still had our fail-safe marked cards to rely on. I never bothered to find out the formula or how George arranged the slug. Another convenient way of burying my head in the sand, of remaining ignorant of all the unpleasant details of our scam.

Scams, like most things, have structure. Define the situation. Act normal. Inspire trust in those you are about to cheat. Make sure the victims think they are in control. Let them open some of the decks, especially the suspicious type. Crack a few jokes. Distract attention at the crucial moments. Ensure you open the deck with the slug in it. Do the false shuffle and cut. It all takes place quickly at the beginning of the game. You need to be fearless, stupid. I couldn't believe I was doing it but the buzz was addictive.

And we did win, like George said, 'Big money. Big, big money.' After the game we would go to his place to divvy up the winnings: forty-five percent each to George and me, ten to Cathy. George would already have the money in piles. We stayed for half an hour, had a drink and laughed, especially when George, giving Cathy her share, always said, 'And this is for the devil woman.'

I'd witnessed crooked market traders sell nylon stockings without feet. I'd watched pitchers conduct *mock auctions,* persuading gullible punters to bid for their own money in a charade that ended up with them going home with a canteen of crap cutlery, a candlewick bedspread and a cuckoo clock. All for the bargain price of a week's wages. George was in a different class, another league, a career card sharp, always on the make. Above all he always gave an award-winning performance, playing his part to perfection.

And like a spectre he would appear without warning. A mystery man. Where did he go when he wasn't with us? Did he have a girlfriend, was he married, did he have a family? Who taught him to be such a brilliant conman? I had no idea. Very occasionally, his mask would slip, especially when we lost – and sometimes we did, despite the chicanery. Then the resentful hyena would bare his fangs and howl.

And me? I saved Jimmy from going back inside. I got my savings back and more.

Everything was hunky-dory and no one was any the wiser.

21

There's a postcard under the table. It's from Denise. It must have been in with her letters and dropped out when I was putting them in the cardboard box. She'd been in Greece for most of the summer and had sent me a card from Naxos saying, 'Why aren't you here with me? Love and Love D xxx.'

♦

Denise had started a postgraduate course in Manchester. We hadn't seen much of each other since that summer. We met up at her place after Christmas, a typical student's flat, crappy furniture, a bit damp, lots of posters on the walls. It was in Didsbury, once quite select. Now the growing student population was taking it over.

We went to see Boris Franks in the Britannia, the huge casino he'd opened in Eccles, outside the city centre. He insisted Denise and I stay for dinner with him. When I asked Boris if he knew a Cypriot called George, 'Why are you asking?' he wanted to know.

I told him I'd been introduced to him by somebody in Newcastle.

He looked at me fiercely. 'If you lie down with dogs you'll get up with fleas remember that.' Then he deliberately changed the subject. 'Well, my lovely Denise, what's happening with you?'

Denise, clearly registered something. Obviously I hadn't breathed a word of the scam to her. She looked at me then carried on talking to Boris about her course.

When we got back to her place, Denise asked me what Boris was going on about. I tried to brush it aside and said, 'It was nothing.'

She wasn't daft. 'It didn't sound like nothing to me.'

Recently there had been a growing tension between us. It wasn't that things had changed dramatically. Maybe I was feeling guilty about Cathy, maybe she was feeling guilty about Greece. I couldn't imagine that she hadn't met somebody on holiday. Completely out of character, she became aggressive towards me, sarcastically asking, 'So what do you think about what's happening in Rhodesia?'

It pissed me off and I said, 'I couldn't give a fuck about

what's happening in Rhodesia,' which wasn't true. I added, 'More important, what do you think about "Yesterday"? I don't mean yesterday Monday, I mean The Beatles' fucking song. And just for the record, I think Ian Smith is a heartless bastard.'

That more or less killed what was left of the evening. We went to bed, didn't even cuddle. I went back to Newcastle in the morning. We were arguing about something else not Rhodesia.

I was an idiot. Our naive attempts at 'free love' had become a problem.

22

What became a much bigger problem was Cathy and George and the scam.

Six months in I realised that on the nights we were cheating I no longer enjoyed dealing. On the nights we weren't cheating I no longer enjoyed dealing either. Still I carried on. But there it was, nagging away, the first thing I thought of when I woke up.

I couldn't get it out of my head. It was there when I was shaving, waiting for the kettle to boil, reading the newspaper. 'It's too late to pull out,' I'd tell myself, over and over. 'I'm doing it and I haven't got a good enough reason for why I'm doing it. Amoral or plain stupid?' When would I stop feeling like this, thinking those thoughts? The days rolled on and I got on with doing whatever I was supposed to be doing, getting the car cleaned, going to the bank, buying another pair of cufflinks. It was no longer the same.

Still I carried on.

Two incidents occurred which changed everything.

George was in, and doing very nicely. It was getting late and the game was all but over when this couple walked in, both expensively dressed, looking like they'd just been to a wedding. George didn't see them at first. When he did, the colour drained out of his face. 'That's me done, I'm finishing now.' He said, very quickly. He stood up and left the room. On the way out he gave the bloke and woman seriously dirty looks. The game finished soon after and the players left.

Not knowing what was going on I carried on stacking the cards, emptying the money from the boxes. The couple came back into the room and the guy said, 'My name's Ronnie and this is Susie. Can I have a word with you?'

'Sure,' I said. 'What do you want?'

'I'd like to look at the cards,' Ronnie said.

'Well you can't,' I said.

'Why not?' he asked.

'Because I said so. Anyway you shouldn't be in here, the game's over.'

'What's the problem?'

'The problem is if you don't get out of here immediately I'll call security and have you escorted out.' I walked to the door, opened it and said, 'Now.'

They both turned and walked out the door. As they passed me Ronnie said, 'George a friend of yours, then?'

Somewhat shaken, I carried on sorting out the money. When Cathy came in to clear away the coffee stuff, I told her to swap the marked cards on the table for the originals in her bag and not ask any questions. We packed up as normal, everything seemed fine, nobody said anything. We left to meet George.

He went mad when I told him what had happened. 'That fucker Ronnie he's out of order, I fix him.' He informed us that Ronnie and his silent friend Susie were card sharps from Leeds. Whether by accident or design they'd come to the club, seen George, assumed something was going on and decided to wind me up. George was confident nothing more would happen and we wouldn't see them again, especially after, as he put it, 'I have words with Ronnie.'

Who else knew about us, I wondered? Was I now part of 'their' world? I was in free fall and I didn't like it one bit.

♦

Two weeks later I arranged to see Denise in Manchester. We'd made up since our argument about Rhodesia. I couldn't wait to see her. I needed to be with her, to get away from what I was doing. She looked beautiful. She was wearing a long Indian skirt with a purple fringed top. Draped around her shoulders was the white mantilla I'd bought her in Las Palmas. She smelt of flowers and sandalwood. I'd booked a room at the

Midland Hotel. We were excited to be with each other. It was like the time we spent at the Santa Catalina.

She looked down at me and said, 'I love you, David M.'

I knew she didn't need me to say it to her. Instead, I said, 'I'm not surprised.'

She punched me on the arm and I grabbed her.

That night we went to Wellingtons, a high-end casino in the city centre. It was Denise's idea to go gambling, which was surprising. She was in high spirits and I guess she wanted to do something she knew I would enjoy. As soon as we went in, Gerry and Sergio, the two owners, came to greet us. They always made a big fuss of me, treating me like I was family. They were both in their forties, dapper, with pencil moustaches and crew cuts. They hadn't met Denise before and were instantly smitten. Gerry found us a table in the bar and ordered a bottle of champagne.

The decor was chic. Deep-blue, plush carpets climbed up the front of a long, intimately lit bar with a pale flag-stone counter. Pendant lights hung from the ceiling like huge floating mushrooms. The bar stools, tables and chairs were shiny, black, fibre glass tulips with maroon cushions and modern paintings covered the walls. Denise kept nudging me, telling me who the paintings were by, asking whether or not I thought they were originals (they weren't). It was very cool, not your average casino. Denise was enjoying herself. Sergio and Gerry had a drink with us, insisted she play roulette and gave her a handful of chips. It was pretty funny watching her serious attempts to play. After she won ten pounds betting even money on the colours, she decided to stop, overwhelmed by her success. Sergio went potty when she tried to give him his money back.

We were going back to our table when Sergio asked if I wanted to play poker. It was an invitation-only game in a private room. Denise gave my arm an encouraging squeeze. He led us to the poker room, through a polythene-covered corridor, past a newly-plastered extension. Business was booming. Like the rest of the casino the poker room was ultra chic.

There were four players already seated, plus a dealer. The game was five-card stud, no limit, five pounds ante – each player putting five pounds in the pot before the cards are dealt. It was a big game. I didn't recognise any of the players except for one, The Shah, one of the most famous professional gamblers in the country. He was in his fifties with thick black hair, a bushy moustache and a deep, honey coloured tan. He was wearing a dinner suit and bow tie and on the little finger of his right hand a gold knot ring, set with a single large sparkling diamond.

Sergio introduced Denise and me to the others and asked if it was okay for Denise to sit near me. Gambling at this level, accompanied by a girlfriend, was not encouraged and something I usually made a point of not doing. But it was a very relaxed atmosphere and we were having fun. We sat down, Denise just behind me at my right elbow.

Sergio said he was going to play and sat in, too. The other three players were middle-aged men: Leonard, an overweight, balding man, Kevin, a tall, skinny, nervous bloke with a distracting twitch in his left eye, and a hard-to-read Asian guy wearing sunglasses who went by the name of Sunglasses.

The dealer was Eyeshadow Joe, from the Whisky A Go Go – only now he didn't wear eye shadow. He'd changed. Before, he'd been softer, now he was tougher, like a successful businessman. It was an all-cash game, no chips. Joe asked me to declare my 'table stakes' - how much money I was putting on the table.The rule being, the amount of money you had to play with in any hand was limited to the amount of money you had sitting on the table. You couldn't add more money to your stack in the middle of a hand. I declared in total nine hundred pounds. I had the smallest float by a long way.

At that time, five-card stud was the most popular variant of poker being played in UK casinos. That night they were playing the standard game. The first card, face down – the hole card. The next card, face up – the first open card. Then the betting starts. The highest hand to bet first. Three more open cards to come, with betting on each round. My golden rules for five-card stud were: tight is right – play the odds; if any of your opponents' open cards beat your hole or open cards, fold; don't throw your money away chasing low straights or flushes.

Occasionally I broke the rules.

Joe was an excellent dealer, quite formal, polite but firm. He handled the cards in a confident, skillful manner, swiftly and accurately, sliding them across the baize to each player. He had certainly come a long way since the Whisky days; he must have been practising. I hadn't seen him for a few years and he made a point of asking how I was getting on, saying how pleased he was to hear that I was doing well.

Sergio was a fantastic host, making sure everybody was being well looked after – drinks, food, cigars, all on the house. I was getting good cards, playing well and after an hour and a half I was winning about three grand. I got involved in a couple of big pots and gave some of it back.

There's something gritty about playing with cash, especially when it's high denomination bank notes – fifties, hundreds or sealed packets of a grand. It's got *oomph* and there's nothing like the feeling of throwing crisp, new one hundred pound notes into the pot, particularly when you know you can't be beat.

I could tell Denise was fighting hard to control her reactions to my winning and losing hands. She would hold her breath when I was involved in any big betting and just about stopped herself from kissing me whenever I won. Except for The Shah, nobody was a top- notch player. He was the only professional, we were all amateurs. I quickly knew I had the edge over the other four and was determined not to cross swords with The Shah unless there was no choice. A strategy confirmed as I watched his geniality change to cold steel as he drew Kevin and Sunglasses into a big pot – before taking them to the cleaners.

I couldn't say when it happened, but I had a slight feeling of unease and was picking up on something odd. At first I wasn't sure exactly what it was, then I realised it was to do with how Sergio was behaving, the way he was presenting himself. He was doing a number, he was acting. We all act, but this was different, he was carefully watching everybody, most of all himself. Trying a bit too hard to assure us how great everything was, 'It's all kosher, don't worry, you're all safe, I'm the generous host and you are my special guests ...' I couldn't think who it was he reminded me of. I was searching for a name, a face, trying to place exactly who it was – somebody I knew? Or an actor, maybe?

Then of course, it hit me. The veil lifted, and it was obvious. George. Sergio was doing a George. He was at the con. I couldn't believe it, but I knew I was right. My mind was racing. What exactly was going on? Was Eyeshadow Joe in on it, or somebody else? I decided to sit it out for a while, play even tighter and observe.

By then we'd been playing for two hours and Joe announced it was time for a new deck – a fairly normal thing to do.

'Comfort break and drinks, everybody,' announced Sergio.

Kevin went out and so did Leonard. A waitress appeared, offering drinks, snacks, cigars. Denise and I went over to a small table that had fruit and water laid out.

'Are you okay?' I asked her.

'I'm fine. You seem to be doing well. You're quite good at it aren't you?' she said, smiling, giving me a hug. When we were in Las Palmas I'd shown her how to play poker, so she did know the game. She looked at me. 'Are you all right? You look a bit tired.'

'I've had enough, I'm going to finish soon,' I said. I kissed her on the cheek and we chatted for a bit, then went back to the table and sat down. The Shah smiled at me, I nodded and smiled back.

A new sealed deck was brought in which Joe opened. He shuffled and then offered the pack to Sergio to cut. Still standing up Sergio just tapped it, meaning no need to cut, just deal.

Nothing unusual in that, other than this all took place as people were moving around and drinks were being served. Define the situation – keep it jolly, distract attention at the crucial moments. A strategy I knew well.

Joe started to deal. I watched, while apparently not watching, relaxing. Regardless of the cards I was dealt I had decided not to play the first hand but as it was I was dealt bad cards. The Shah also folded early on. There were four players left in: Sergio, Kevin, Leonard and Sunglasses. I'd played with Sergio many times, a very experienced, very cautious player. But the way he played this hand could only be described as reckless, like that of a total beginner. Completely out of character he continued to play a hand he should have folded after the first open card, called large bets against all the odds and made a final bet that was questionable by any stretch of the imagination. Despite heavy betting, he stayed in the hand with un-matching low cards against three other players all showing good cards – Kevin and Leonard showing high pairs, jacks and tens respectively (there were no other jacks or tens showing) and Sunglasses with a possible king flush in diamonds (there were no other diamonds showing). After the last open card, Sergio bet into the three other players. Any one of them could have beaten him. Sunglasses folded and in the showdown Kevin revealed two pairs - jacks and nines. Leonard also had two pairs – queens and tens. Against all the odds, Sergio had three sixes. On the second and last open cards Sergio had connected to his hole card - a six.

Sergio won the pot.

And this, the first pot after the break was big. The biggest pot of the night. In fact, at over seven grand - enough for a nice house and a new E-Type Jag.

The Shah, who had not shown a flicker of emotion all evening, registered surprise. I'm sure, like me, it was not because of the size of the pot, or that Sergio had made three sixes, but because of the way Sergio had played the hand – as if he knew everyone else's hole cards and knew what was coming.

My suspicions gave rise to immediate questions. Was the deck rigged? Especially as it was the first hand with a new pack. Was Joe dealing seconds? He gripped the pack in such a way that the edge of the second card from the top was easy to see and it allowed him to deal the second rather than the top card of the deck. Were the cards marked? I couldn't say for sure and I wasn't about to do a Ronnie and ask to examine them. They were using unusual decks. Very classy, probably custom made. The backs a soft purple colour, with five large daisies in the centre, surrounded by lobed leaves, bordered by an inner white line, then an outer pale purple line. On the very outside a deep purple border of intertwined leaves, 1920s style. Easy to mark.

It wasn't just the way Sergio played, or the way he was behaving. It was the way I felt. Maybe I was paranoid, but my guts were churning and my brain was telling me to *get out*. Instinct is a very accurate barometer and I was not about to ignore it. Something was going on, no question about it.

Wellingtons, like so many early sixties casinos, was owned and run like a small family business. In just a few years casinos and nightclubs with gaming had grown out of all proportion. An estimated one thousand casinos had opened in the last five years. People all over the UK were gambling for high stakes.

Any night, anywhere, you could walk into a club, have a drink, watch a show and gamble. It may not have had the glitz and glamour of Monte Carlo or Las Vegas but fortunes were being won and lost in provincial cities and small towns throughout the country. It was new and nobody was checking anything, not the cards, not the roulette wheels, not the police records of owners or croupiers. With no proper controls it was like playing three-card brag at home with a few pals. There were few if any regulations, little or no supervision of gambling establishments, leaving them wide open to cheating and ripe pickings for unscrupulous owners, card cheats and crooked croupiers.

As well I knew.

Still, I was shocked. Sergio and Gerry treated me like a son. They were caring and generous, concerned about my welfare, always asking after my mother and sisters. Their business was hugely successful. *Why* would they be involved in this stuff? For the same reason I was, I reasoned. Greed. Pure greed.

Obviously I wasn't going to say anything. I just needed to leave.

I leaned over to Denise and whispered, 'I'm going to the loo then I'm finishing.' She looked at me and nodded. I said to Joe, 'Deal me out Joe, I'm going to the loo.' I went out, washed my face, stayed awhile, came back and said, 'Sorry about this, but I don't feel very well. I'm gonna have to quit.' I picked up my money, thanked everybody for the game, and we left. If I had any doubts about my decision they were quickly dispelled when I saw The Shah picking up his money, also preparing to leave.

I was a casebook victim: turned over in something I knew about, conned by people I trusted. My immediate emotions ran from feeling a total chump to frustration and anger. It made me feel oddly sad and unsettled.

Sergio followed Denise and me and caught up with us as we were about to leave. 'Are you all right, David, can I get you anything?' he asked.

I said, 'It's okay Sergio, it must have been something I ate, I feel sick. We're going. I'll be fine.'

I did feel sick.

23

It was a mild evening and a full moon. We held hands as we walked back to the Midland, only a few minutes away. The town hall clock struck eleven as we crossed St. Peter's Square. Denise asked me what was really the matter. She could tell there was more to it than me saying I felt sick. I said I'd explain when we got back to the hotel.

The bad feeling was growing. That was me, back there, dealing. Not Eyeshadow Joe. And the players weren't Leonard, The Shah, Sunglasses and Kevin, either. They were Tommy, Ike, Bing, Alec ... and all those people I had been entertaining.

And cheating.

Denise listened in silence when I told her what happened in the game, how I knew what Sergio and Joe were doing. I told her about Cathy, George, everything. She didn't say anything. When I'd finished she said she was tired and wanted to go to bed. I said I was going downstairs for a drink.

I sat on my own, in the huge empty lounge, drinking coffee and brandy. A few years ago it's where I'd have been with my pals, fooling around, playing at having money, surrounded by overweight people, sitting in overstuffed chairs, eating overpriced desserts. We'd avoid the evil eye of Tony the head waiter and make one drink last hours and, much to the annoyance of the pianist, would sing along to "Fly Me To The Moon". Sidney Sherman would have himself paged, 'Telephone call for Mr Sidney Sherman ... paging Mr Sidney Sherman,' leaving it for ages, letting the waiter repeat his name, making sure everybody had heard it. Then off he would go to the reception to take a call from his brother or some other *meshugenah* he'd set it up with. Knowing full well what a bullshitter he was, of course we questioned him about the call. Was somebody ill, was it the mystery girl from Kendal's he claimed fancied him, maybe it was the Chief Rabbi or the Pope? We would always push it to the absurd and Sidney would play it for real. A fantasist, he went to great lengths to back up his delusions and being paged in a posh hotel proved to himself he was somebody.

Sitting now in the silent lounge, Denise up in the room, memories taking me back to being eighteen, I couldn't help but think about what had happened to me. Never mind Sidney Sherman, who was I pretending to be? I ordered more brandy and coffee, smoked a cigar. The night waiter was an old man, he looked tired and I felt guilty. I looked blankly round the empty room, random memories running through my head ... *I once kept the same taxi all day while I went shopping in London ... I put on a jacket I hadn't worn for weeks and found a hundred pounds I'd forgotten about in one of the pockets ... Whenever I caught the sleeper to London I gave the guard a fiver to make sure I didn't have to share.*

Money to burn, mixing with celebrities, dream cars, I had it all. I was young and smart, yet stupid enough to have taken unnecessary, unacceptable risks. I'd made a big mistake and I knew it. It was my mistake, nobody else was to blame and I knew what I had to do.

I had to get away from Cathy and George.

Maybe telling Denise everything had been the first step. I didn't know for sure, but I'd done it now and there was no going back. I was glad, and I felt better. That might have been the brandy, though.

The waiter came back to see if I wanted anything else but I'd been there two hours and I'd had enough. I gave him a tenner. He looked at it, looked at me, shook his head in surprise, smiled and nodded.

When I got back to the room Denise was asleep.

The next morning we had breakfast and then I took Denise back to her place. It felt odd that we didn't talk about it. We didn't talk about anything really. I asked her what she was doing. She said she had an essay to finish and was going into college. She asked me what I was doing. I said I was driving back and going to work that evening. As she went to get out the car she kissed me on the cheek and said, 'Drive carefully.'

'Is that it?' I asked her. 'Are we not going to discuss it?'

'There's nothing to discuss,' Denise replied.

'What about us? How do you feel ...'

'I feel disappointed, David, that's how I feel. Disappointed!' she retorted and quickly got out the car and ran into the house.

My first report at the grammar school had read, 'A disappointing first term.' I stayed in the bottom class for the next five years. 'Disappointed' seemed such a mild expression compared to 'arsehole', 'liar', 'crook', any of which Denise could have used. Yet it hung in the air with unrelenting condemnation, all-embracing sadness, regret, unfulfilled expectations. She was the best thing that had happened to me and I'd let her down. I sat in the car with an overwhelming sense of loss. Denise embodied true beauty and integrity, everything I wanted. And I'd thrown it away. I needed to talk to somebody.

◆

I went to see Wolfie. He opened the door. He was covered in paint. I followed him into his studio.

He was working on a large landscape painting about 9ft by 6ft. The background was bright yellow and the roughly drawn figures and objects were in black and white. In the foreground a boy of about fifteen was sitting on a table, sewing a button on a shirt. Underneath the table, an elderly couple, two young men and a young girl, were lying asleep. A teenage girl was standing behind the boy with her back to him. She was looking round at the boy as she was taking her top off.

It perfectly captured my own mood of deep sadness.

Wolfie stood looking at the painting for minutes then turned to me and said, 'What's the problem?'

I told him everything.

He laughed. 'The *yeshiva bocher* turned dealer has now turned card sharp. What next, bank robber? Assassin?' He laughed again.

'It's not funny,' I said.

'Not for those you cheated,' he agreed. 'Why tell me? Why tell Denise?'

'I dunno,' I said.

'Yes you do. Confession. You wanted to confess. Well, you've done it and it doesn't change anything. You're a fool. You got into bed with George the *ganef*, and there's a price to pay.' He smiled. 'It's not the end of the world, David. Whatever he took from you, whatever you gave him, you're alive and still have your brain. It's time to use it. Now, do you want a tea before you go and leave me to carry on with my masterpiece?'

'No. I'm going,' I said.

He opened the front door to let me out, patted me on the cheek and said, 'It's life, David. Be a *mensch*. Do what's right.' He shut the door.

I drove back through Leeds, up to Scotch Corner and on the dual carriageway doing a hundred and ten I took my hands off the wheel, the Mercedes was as steady as a rock. I wasn't and I knew it. By the time I reached Newcastle I was ready to do what I had to do.

... It was two years before he came out of that place. That place that one day some would say never existed. He went back to his village and waited for someone to return. No one came, and nobody believed his story. After a year he left again. He never found out what happened to his beautiful cousin, or his aunt, but he had seen what had happened to his parents, sister, and brothers.

He knew enough.

24

Maple Court, 11:10 a.m.

I write a brief note to Ella and Marty giving them Rita's number in case of anything, reminding them what a great housekeeper Mrs Henderson is. I put the note pad and pen in my case. I will keep them.

I'd always thought the punters were the mugs but I'm the mug. I was – am – the one that had the most to lose, not George or Cathy. And it was much, much more than money or a job.

Too late now.

25

After leaving Wolfie I got back about nine in the evening and went straight to the club.

Harry and Joseph always asked me what was happening in Manchester, how my mother was, what I'd done. They gave me my share of the tips even when I hadn't been there. Remorse, guilt, I had it in spades. It's amazing how stupid, careless, blind, you can be.

When Cathy came in I told her we needed to meet. She knew there was something up.

She said, 'Okay, let's go back to yours.'

That wasn't what I wanted but I thought, what's the difference? Let's get it over with. As soon as we got in the flat she said, 'What's going on?'

'I've decided I'm not going to carry on doing this stuff with George.'

'Really, why not?'

'I've had enough, that's why.'

'What about me? And George? Don't we have a say?'

'No you don't,' I said. 'I take all the risks and I've had enough.'

She looked at me hard, then laughed. I was standing by the window. She came over to me, 'What's the matter, did something happen in Manchester?'

'Nothing happened, I just can't do it anymore.'

'I'll stay, we can talk about it,' she said.

I could tell she wanted to have sex and I could feel myself responding but I had to see this through. 'I don't want you to,' I said.

She knew what I meant. 'You mean you don't want to fuck me anymore.'

'That's right.'

'Oh dear, no cheating, no fucking. Mr Goody Two Shoes,' she mocked.

'I wish I'd never met you and fucking George,' I said.

'So we forced you to do it, did we? Take all that money, buy all your flash jewellery and cars.'

'No, you didn't, I had all that shit before I met you. I should never have got involved with you and your crooked brother.'

'Don't bring Jimmy into this,' she screamed.

We stood glaring at each other. It was over and we both knew it. 'You'll never get anybody like me again,' she said bitterly. 'I should have known, you're all the same you lot.'

'That's right,' I said and walked out of the room. There was a 24 hour taxi firm next to the flat. I called them and she left.

Naively I thought that was that. I could just put a stop to it all. I hadn't thought any further.

The next morning, though, Jimmy rang and said he wanted to talk to me. He came round to my place that afternoon. He said Cathy had told him what had been going on. He said he didn't see why I couldn't turn a blind eye and let Cathy carry on switching the cards with George.

He didn't get it.

All I knew was that I was now discussing what I should do with my life, with Jimmy, a petty crook. This was how far I'd fallen. 'I don't want to talk to you about any of this,' I told him.

He said, 'I think you should. You wouldn't want this to get out.'

The creep was trying to do a number on me! If it wasn't for me he'd be in jail. I knew then that what I had to do would have to be far more drastic than anything I'd thought of so far. 'Listen to me carefully,' I said. I was quite calm. 'I don't want to see you again. If you try to come into the club I'll have you thrown out. And another thing, you tell Cathy to go on holiday for the next two weeks – ring in sick – I don't care – but she's not to come back until I've left the club. Do you understand what I'm saying? Now piss off.'

He looked at me and sneered. 'You Yids are all the same, you do everything to suit yourselves.'

That's when I lost it. I don't really remember what happened next, only that I had him by the throat and was pulling his tie tight. 'Let me go, let me go, you mad bastard.' He was gasping for air.

I let go. 'Get out, get out,' I shouted.

He scurried off.

I sat on the sofa trying to calm down, horrified at my lack of self control. My head filling with all the old venom I'd heard so many times, '*Dirty, greedy Jew, you killed Christ,*' the vicious name calling from kids in the street. Then later, the dangerous, anti-semitic falsehoods, '*All Jews are wealthy, Jews own the banks,*' and on and on. This, from supposed friends, people I'd worked with, individuals from all walks of life, regardless of class or intellect. When challenged it had on occasion ended in a punch up or prompted the usual, 'I don't mean you, you're different ... Some of my best friends are Jews.' It made me wary, like a badly treated animal.

Jimmy's visit had brought home to me that the mess I'd got myself in could not be sorted out so easily. After ten minutes I rang Harry and Joseph and said I needed to talk to them. Whether it was impulsive, I don't know. Maybe deep down this *was* what I really wanted – to have no alternative, but to get out.

I'd always liked Harry and Joseph, they were lovely men, hard-working, honest, generous, and devoted to each other. Sure, they made a few bad decisions, took risks, what's new? Show me a successful businessman who hasn't had failures or skated on thin ice. It was Harry who set it up so that I was paying tax on earnings thirty times lower than what I should have declared. Where does that sit on the scam scale? Mind you, nobody likes the taxman. Even rock stars were whinging on about him and the biggest tax dodgers of all were – are – the banks.

I marvelled at my own thoughts, dollops of detachment, denial, self-justification. But what was irrefutable was that I'd betrayed those close to me.

Harry and Joseph lived in comfort, in a Regency style block of flats. They'd had money for a long time and it showed. The lounge was split level, with two huge white sofas, a large glass coffee table and a veranda window overlooking an expansive, well-tended, lush garden. I sat on one of the sofas opposite both of them.

'Well, what's the matter, David?' Harry was like that, straight in.

'There's a scam happening, to do with marked cards. We need to change our cards to plain backs,' I told him.

'How d'you know?' asked Joseph.

'I found out in Manchester. It's happening all over the place. We can get hold of plain backs without any trouble.

And another thing, we need to keep an eye on George, he's dodgy.'

'Right. Anything else?' Harry looked at me.

'I'm going to have to pack it in,' I said.

'What are you talking about?' Joseph demanded.

'I need to be at home more. It's to do with my mother. I'm going to have to go back to Manchester.'

'Surely, we can work something out?' Joseph asked.

'Leave it Joseph, let David deal with this,' Harry said. He knew there was more to it than I was saying. He looked at me again. 'Don't rush anything David, think about it. Nobody's perfect.' Clever Harry.

I moved fast. Ella and Marty loved my place and agreed to take over the flat and all my stuff within a couple of weeks. I went to Manchester told my mother and Rita that I was getting out of the gambling business and was going away. I didn't know where exactly. I wanted to travel and would make sure there was enough money to take care of things. They just accepted it and didn't ask any questions. My mother was delighted.

I often loaned money to regulars and three of them owed me quite a bit, but I wrote it off. Paul, one of the croupiers, bought my suits. Rick, the bandleader bought my jewellery. I advertised the Mercedes. It was a dream car. There weren't many fancy cars around and I'd often come back to where I'd parked to find a couple of people checking it out, admiring it.

Two buyers, this big bloke and his bigger son showed up at the flat. I let them both have a drive even though the whole time I was paranoid and thought they were going to do me in. They gave me cash and drove away my elegant Mercedes Coupé, forever.

It had been a lot quicker getting rid of all my gear than it had been acquiring it and nowhere near as much fun.

At three in the morning the telephone rang. I answered it, nobody said anything but I knew it was Cathy. After the second night it happened, I disconnected the phone before going to bed.

My last night in the club – my last night in the gambling business – I looked at it with new eyes. It was no longer glamorous. It was just a big room in an ugly sixties building down a small town alleyway. I knew I wouldn't miss it. I would never forget it, but that was different. It was like any other mid-week night, not that busy, an early finish. I took a cab home, disconnected the phone, went to bed and dreamed.

It seemed a simple enough dream. I had the core of a cabbage embedded in my head. About four inches long and one inch thick, set in on the right side, at a slight angle, it protruded just enough for me to get my finger tips round it. I attempted to pull it out. At first it wouldn't move, then with a strong tug it was free. I woke up immediately and touched the side of my head. With a great sense of relief there was nothing there. I realised it was a dream. It was so vivid that a couple of times that day I touched the spot where it had been to reassure myself it had gone.

The dream left me with a good feeling.

26

Maple Court, 11:45 a.m.

Suddenly there's only fifteen minutes to go. I feel good. I must have had a nap.

For some reason I take the CND badge that Denise gave me out of the jewellery box.

I pin it on my T-shirt. It's the first time I've worn it. Why not?

I scoop up the few things left on the table. After sealing and tying up the cardboard box I sit down and wait.

I hear the taxi and look out the window to check. He's early - good. The phone rings again.

'David?' It's Denise.

'Yes.'

'What's going on? Your mother told me that you've left

the club and are going away.' She sounded upset.

'That's right.'

'Why didn't you tell me?'

'I didn't want to.'

'Why?'

'Because I love you, that's why,' I said.

'Then why are you leaving?'

'Because I have to sort this out on my own. I can't talk now, I've got to go, I'll ring you.' I put the phone down slowly.

I go into the kitchen wash the brandy glass, throw the cigar stub into the waste bin and wash the ashtray. Go back into the lounge, wait a moment, look round the room, pick up the cardboard box and the suitcase, walk out the door, lock it, put the keys through the letter box and run down the three flights of stairs to the waiting taxi.

It is exactly nineteen years since Bernie asked me to hold his watch.

... He was still a teenager when a waitress serving him coffee saw him staring at the five blurred numbers, crudely tattooed on her left forearm. She looked into his eyes and said, 'Yes ... can I help you?' He pushed up the left sleeve of his cardigan offered her his forearm, smiled sadly and quietly said, 'Snap.'

They became friends, then lovers.

27

London, March 9, 2020, 8:45 p.m.

Another chance event like before.

Two weeks before the first lockdown, I'd been invited to the opening of a play in London, a theatre on the Strand. In the interval I was standing in the doorway of the bar when I saw Joseph. It *couldn't* be Joseph ... but it was? Then I realised the young man in question was in his late thirties. Joseph would be over eighty now. The man was tall, handsome, looked Spanish and carried himself in exactly the same way as Joseph had. It was uncanny. The only difference was this young man's bohemian appearance, scruffier than Joseph ever would have been.

I felt compelled to speak to him and elbowed my way into the room. He was talking to an attractive older woman. I stopped in front of them. Turning to the young man I said,

'I'm sorry to interrupt, but you don't know somebody called Joseph Rose, do you?'

He looked at me in surprise and said, 'He was my father.'

The woman turned to me and said, 'And he was my husband.'

She looked comfortable in herself. I smiled and said to the young man, 'You look so much like your father. I knew him many years ago. We worked together in nightclubs. My name is David Malkowski ... it used to be Mall when I worked in clubs.'

'I'm Anthony,' the young man said, 'Dad was always talking about you. Shall we meet here in the bar after the show?'

'Yes, let's meet again.' The woman said. She stared at me and added quietly, 'I'm Denise.'

And the bell rang for the Second Act.

As they walk out of the bar, I am unable to move. I watch them go up the stairs leading to the Circle. I am aware of people brushing past me and I hear the final bell. Eventually, I look round the empty bar and sit down by a window table, not knowing what to do with myself. I stand up again, order a large brandy and a coffee.

♦

I haven't seen Denise since that day in Manchester, a lifetime ago, when she told me she was 'disappointed'. My mind is in turmoil. Denise and Joseph married. When? Why? How was that possible? So many questions.

I'd gone to great lengths to try and find her. I'd first tried in 1976 when I had come back to England to see my mother who was seriously ill. Then more recently, five years ago, I came back here permanently and had spent several days in Manchester Central library going through electoral rolls, telephone directories searching for Denise.

Nothing.

In Heron House, across Albert Square, you can buy local birth, marriage and death certificates. By obtaining Denise's birth certificate I found her mother's details. Then, assuming her mother had probably died, I searched for and found the death certificate in the hope that Denise might have signed it giving an address.

Nothing.

I checked out all the social media and online ancestry tracing sites. I even contacted an agency but as Tony from Search Services eventually pointed out, 'No can do, I'm afraid. It's always difficult and with a woman there's the problem of a possible name change, compounded by the passage of time.'

I paid up and gave up.

I'm lost in the past, in my imagination of what could happen next. The coffee and brandy are helping – but a cigar, a Romeo y Julieta, how lovely that would be. I haven't smoked for over fifty years. Fribourg and Treyer is long gone. I'd seen it that very morning. All that remains of their exquisite three hundred year old shop is the front facade of bow windows and bevelled window panes. On one pane, their faded name struggles to be recognised. Inside, the humidors and cigars have been replaced by MDF shelving filled with toy black taxis, red buses, I Love London T-shirts, countless tourist knick-knacks.

Why had I taken such drastic action all those years ago? Why had I found it necessary to extricate myself completely from the world of gambling? I like to think it was because I was choosing to start a better life. In some way making amends and righting the wrong of betraying those who trusted me. Would I have taken the action if things had been different? What if I hadn't witnessed Sergio and Eyeshadow Joe cheating? If Denise hadn't been with me that night? If I hadn't had the run in with Jimmy?

I continued to face a dilemma which had never really gone away. I saw myself in a duel with myself which often led me into taking risks of all kinds. I had to be on my guard, always. I accepted responsibility for my actions. I knew that circumstances, other people and chance, had intervened to save me from myself.

Chance or choice? I didn't know. I didn't know what had brought me to this moment in my life. Whatever it was, I didn't believe that it was part of some divine plan.

I can't believe I've found Denise at last.

Sitting there in the Circle bar, I think of Wolfie Goldschmidt, my gambling mentor. Wolfie was another one I hadn't seen again after my confession. He'd gone to America and become a successful artist, his paintings selling for thousands of dollars. He, who had lost everything, was in no doubt. He never failed to remind me how, 'It makes no difference David, how good you are, how clever you are, what you've done, where you've been, where you're going. Life, like chemmy is just a game of chance.'

I never saw any of those people from my past life again. I thought about them, dreamt about them but like characters in a movie they remained in another reality. That's not to say that what had happened didn't affect my life. It did. It coloured my view of the world, of people and events. It made me question my own desire for success and fame of any kind. I never doubted that somehow I had managed to escape an unfortunate, degrading existence. I never regretted getting out and from then on money and power ceased to impress me.

But – Denise.

The misgivings are starting. I wonder if another brandy will help. I've read about trying to reconnect with past lovers, how addictive it can be, how out of control the mind can be. How renewed past encounters supposedly activate hormones that unleash a network of brain activity, driving us to repeat pleasurable experiences. Add to that age, nostalgia, a desire to rewrite history and you have a heady cocktail of trouble.

Maybe, I thought, I should go.

Then suddenly, Denise is there, standing in front of me and that is reality.

'I couldn't sit through the second half, wondering whether or not you would still be here when we came out,' she says. 'Anthony will join us later. I need a drink.' Simple words that chase away all my thoughts.

I stand up, looking into her face, searching for the young woman I once knew and for a second there she is ... then she is gone and another woman, someone I don't know is smiling at me.

'Sorry, what would you like?' I ask her.

'A large gin and tonic, please.' Then she asks, 'Is it really you, David?'

'I think so,' I say. 'Let me get your drink.' I go to the bar, knowing Denise has been watching me as I get back to the table and sit down.

'I'm finding this very surreal,' she says.

'You and me both.' I am unable to stop looking at her. She is an extremely attractive, older woman, beautifully dressed. With a shock I realise she is wearing a pearl necklace I remember buying for her – if it is the same one. She sees me looking.

'It's the one you bought me for my nineteenth birthday, I had it shortened,' she tells me. There is a pause, then she says, 'This is getting weirder by the minute. I spent quite a bit of time trying to find you, David, especially after Joseph died.'

'And I spent a long time trying to find you – well, trying to find Denise White. I didn't know you'd become Denise Rose.'

She looks at me. 'When you disappeared I went to Newcastle to see if anybody knew anything and that's when I met Joseph.' She gently puts her hand on mine and carries on talking, 'After Joseph died five years ago, I tried again to trace you. There was nobody left to ask and no David Mall or Malkowski I came across matched you. Joseph never stopped talking about you, you know.'

'And I never stopped thinking about him and you. How strange that there you were, together.'

We talk easily, about the people we once knew and how life had been for us. She tells me that she'd had a good life with Joseph, that they'd had the one son, Anthony, and were very happy. Joseph carried on in the nightclub business for a few years, then moved into property development before retiring twenty years ago. I told her that I'd become an academic, lived with different women, had no children, was happy, and that I'd been on my own for six years.

As a camera lens moves in and out of focus, sometimes I can see, just for a passing moment, the passionate girl I'd drunk champagne cocktails with in the tropical gardens of the Santa Catalina.

Who does she see, I wonder.

We are both laughing at the story of Sidney Sherman paging himself, when Anthony arrives. 'Glad you two are having a good time, the second half was ... 'crap',' he mouths. 'There's a first night party, do you fancy going? It's somewhere round here.'

We both look at him as if he is mad.

'Why don't you go sweetie?' Denise replies. 'David and I need to catch up.'

Thank God. I was about to suggest that I would go and leave them to continue with their evening. Anthony seems quite happy to go alone. He makes arrangements to see his mother the next day, kisses us both and leaves.

Denise is staying just across the road at the Savoy. She wouldn't dream of staying with Anthony, she says. He lives like a student, above a kebab shop somewhere near Kings Cross.

We just sit looking at each other, time slipping away. I don't know what to say or do.

'What would you like to do, David?' Denise asks me.

'I'd like to hold you in my arms as soon as possible,' I hear myself say.

'What a wonderful idea. Let's go.' She laughs and stands up, ready to leave.

I get up too, overcome with my unexpected good fortune. I know I might be riding the time machine of recaptured youth, and that whatever imagination or recollection tells me about the Denise I last saw over fifty years ago, I have no understanding of who she is today. Yet, for better or worse, the women in my life always influenced me the most. A cherished loved one has re-appeared from the past and is holding out her hand to me.

I take it.